Raspberry Pi 3

Basic to Advanced Projects

Dogan Ibrahim

an Elektor Publication

LEARN | DESIGN | SHARE

● This is an Elektor Publication. Elektor is the media brand of
Elektor International Media B.V.
78 York Street, London W1H 1DP, UK
Phone: (+44) (0)20 7692 8344

● Declaration
The author and publisher have used their best efforts in ensuring the correctness of the information contained in this book. They do not assume, or hereby disclaim, any liability to any party for any loss or damage caused by errors or omissions in this book, whether such errors or omissions result from negligence, accident or any other cause.

● British Library Cataloguing in Publication Data
A catalogue record for this book is available from the British Library

● **ISBN 978-1-907920-67-7**

© Copyright 2018: Elektor International Media b.v.
Prepress Production: D-Vision, Julian van den Berg
First published in the United Kingdom 2018
Printed in the Netherlands by Wilco

Elektor is part of EIM, the world's leading source of essential technical information and electronics products for pro engineers, electronics designers, and the companies seeking to engage them. Each day, our international team develops and delivers high-quality content - via a variety of media channels (e.g., magazines, video, digital media, and social media) in several languages - relating to electronics design and DIY electronics. **www.elektor.com**

LEARN | DESIGN | SHARE

PREFACE

The Raspberry Pi 3 is the latest credit-card sized computer that can be used in many applications, such as in audio and video media centers, as a desktop computer, in industrial controllers, robotics, and in many domestic and commercial applications. In addition to its many features found in other Raspberry Pi computers, the Raspberry Pi 3 also offers Wi-Fi and Bluetooth capability which makes it highly desirable in remote and Internet based control and monitoring applications.

This book is about the Raspberry Pi 3 computer and its use in various control and monitoring applications. The book explains in simple terms and with tested and working example projects, how to configure the Raspberry Pi 3 computer, how to install and use the Linux operating system, and how to write applications programs using the Python programming language.

The book starts with an introduction to the Raspbery Pi 3 computer and covers the topics of installing the operating system on an SD card. Use of the command language and the desktop GUI has been described with examples.
The remaining parts of the book covers many Raspberry Pi 3 based hardware projects using the latest hardware modules such as the Sense HAT, Swiss Pi, Camera module, MotoPi, Bluetooth, Wi-Fi and others. Example projects are given on using the Wi-Fi and the Bluetooth modules to send environmental data to the Cloud, and to communicate with Android based mobile phones.

All the projects given in the book have been tested and are working. The following sub-headings are used in every project:

- Project title
- Project description
- Aim of the project
- Raspberry Pi type
- Block diagram
- Circuit diagram
- Program listing

I hope the readers find the book helpful and enjoy reading it.

Prof Dr Dogan Ibrahim
January, 2018
London.

About the Author

Prof Dr Dogan Ibrahim has BSc degree in electronic engineering, an MSc degree in automatic control engineering, and a PhD degree in digital signal processing. Dogan has worked in many industrial organizations before he returned to academic life. Prof Ibrahim is the author of over 60 technical books and over 200 technical articles on microcontrollers, microprocessors, and related fields. He is a Chartered electrical engineer and a Fellow of the Institution of Engineering Technology.

CHAPTER 1 • RASPBERRY PI MODELS

1.1 Overview

The Raspberry Pi is a low-cost, single-board, powerful computer, capable of running a full operating system and also capable of doing everything that a laptop or a desktop computer can do, such as creating and editing documents, getting on the Internet, receiving and sending mails, playing games, developing programs to monitor and control its environment via electronic sensors and actuators, and many more.

There are several different models of the Raspberry Pi available, each having slightly different features. The fundamental features of all the raspberry Pi computers are similar, all using ARM processors, all having the operating system installed on an SD card, all having on-board memory, and input-output interface connectors. Some models, such as the Raspberry Pi 3 and Raspberry Pi Zero W have built-in Wi-Fi and Bluetooth capabilities, making them easy to get online and to communicate with similar devices having Wi-Fi or Bluetooth capabilities.

In this book we shall be concentrating on the most advanced model, which is the Raspberry Pi 3. All the projects developed in this book will run on this model. Some of the projects may or may not run on the lower models, but necessary information will be given at the beginning of each project.

In this Chapter we shall take a look at the features of the different models of the Raspberry Pi computer.

1.2 Raspberry Pi 1 Model A

This model (Figure 1.1), released in 2013 has the following features:

SOC:	Broadcom BCM2835
Processor:	ARM1176JZF-S
No of cores:	1
CPU clock:	700 MHz
RAM:	256 MB
Camera interface	
USB ports:	1
HDMI ports:	1
Composite video	
SD/MMC:	SD card
GPIO:	26 pins
Current:	200 mA
Cost:	$20

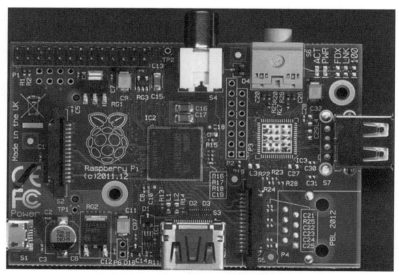

Figure 1.1 Raspberry Pi 1 Model A

1.3 Raspberry Pi 1 Model A+

This model (see Figure 1.2) was released in 2014 and it has the following basic features:

SOC:	Broadcom BCM2835
Processor:	ARM1176JZF-S
No of cores:	1
CPU clock:	700 MHz
RAM:	256 MB
Camera interface	
USB ports:	1
HDMI ports:	1
Composite video	
SD/MMC:	microSD card
GPIO:	40 pins
Current:	200 mA
Cost:	$20

Figure 1.2 Raspberry Pi 1 Model A+

1.4 Raspberry Pi 1 Model B

This model (see Figure 1.3) was released in 2012 and it has the following features:

SOC: Broadcom BCM2835
Processor: ARM1176JZF-S
No of cores: 1
CPU clock: 700 MHz
RAM: 512 MB
USB ports: 2
HDMI ports: 1
Ethernet ports: 1
Camera interface
Composite video
SD/MMC: SD card
GPIO: 26 pins
Current: 700 mA
Cost: $25

Figure 1.3 Raspberry Pi 1 Model B

1.5 Raspberry Pi 1 Model B+

This model (see Figure 1.4) was released in 2014 and it has the following features:

SOC:	Broadcom BCM2835
Processor:	ARM1176JZF-S
No of cores:	1
CPU clock:	700 MHz
RAM:	512 MB
USB ports:	4
HDMI ports:	1
Camera interface	
Composite video	
Ethernet ports:	1
SD/MMC:	microSD card
GPIO:	40 pins
Current:	700 mA
Cost:	$25

Figure 1.4 Raspberry Pi 1 Model B+

1.6 Raspberry Pi 2 Model B

This model (see Figure 1.5) was released in 2015 and it has larger memory, more USB ports, and a faster processor:

SOC:	Broadcom BCM2836
Processor:	Cortex-A7
No of cores:	4
CPU clock:	900 MHz
RAM:	1 GB
USB ports:	4
Ethernet ports:	1
HDMI ports:	1
Camera interface	
Composite video	
SD/MMC:	microSD card
GPIO:	40 pins
Current:	800 mA
Cost:	$35

Figure 1.5 Raspberry Pi 2 Model B

1.7 Raspberry Pi Zero

This model (see Figure 1.6) was released in 2015 and it is a smaller board than the others, but has a fast processor. Its main features are:

SOC:	Broadcom BCM2835
Processor:	ARM1176JZF-S
No of cores:	1
CPU clock:	1 GHz
RAM:	512 MB
USB ports:	1 (micro)
Camera interface	
HDMI ports:	1 (mini)
SD/MMC:	microSD card
GPIO:	40 pins
Current:	160 mA
Cost:	$5

Figure 1.6 Raspberry Pi Zero

1.8 Raspberry Pi 3 Model B

This model (see Figure 1.7) was released in 2016 and it is has the fastest processor speed of all the current models. Its main features are:

SOC:	Broadcom BCM2837
Processor:	Cortex A-53
No of cores:	4
CPU clock:	1.2 GHz
RAM:	1 GB
USB ports:	4
Ethernet ports:	1
HDMI ports:	1
Camera interface	
Composite video	
Wi-Fi	
Bluetooth	
SD/MMC:	microSD card
GPIO:	40 pins
Current:	1.34 A
Cost:	$35

Figure 1.7 Raspberry Pi 3 Model B

1.9 Raspberry Pi Zero W

This is the latest model (see Figure 1.8), released in 2017, and it is a small board (half the size of Model A+) with low current consumption, but has surprising amount of power. Its main advantages are the on-board Wi-Fi and Bluetooth connectivity. The basic features of this model are:

SOC:	Broadcom BCM2835
Processor:	ARM1176JZF-S
No of cores:	1
CPU clock:	1 GHz
RAM:	512 MB
USB ports:	2 (micro)
Camera interface	
HDMI ports:	1 (mini)
Wi-Fi	
Bluetooth	
SD/MMC:	microSD card
GPIO:	40 pins
Current:	180 mA
Cost:	$10

Figure 1.8 Raspberry Pi Zero W

1.10 Summary

In this Chapter we had a look at the basic features of the different models of the Raspberry Pi computer. It is recommended to use the small and low-cost latest model Raspberry Pi Zero W for Wi-Fi or Bluetooth based applications where 512 MB RAM and 1 GHz clock speed are sufficient. For higher speed and more memory requirements the slightly more expensive Raspberry Pi 3 is recommended, and this is the model that is used in all the projects in this book.

CHAPTER 2 • INSTALLING THE OPERATING SYSTEM ON RASPBERRY PI 3

2.1 Overview
In this Chapter we shall see how to load and setup the Raspbian operating system on a microSD card for the Raspberry Pi 3. But before doing that it is worthwhile to look at the components of the Raspberry Pi 3 in a little bit more detail.

2.2 The Raspberry Pi 3 Board
Figure 2.1 shows the Raspberry Pi 3 board with the major components marked. Some details on each component are given in this section.

Figure 2.1 Raspberry Pi 3 board

USB ports: The Raspberry Pi 3 has 4 USB ports to connect mouse, keyboard, webcam etc.

Ethernet and Wi-Fi: Although the Raspberry Pi 3 has built-in Wi-Fi, it can also directly be connected to a router through an Ethernet cable connected to this socket.

Audio/Video Jack: A headphone or a speaker can be connected to this 3.5mm socket. This socket also carries composite video interface.

CSI: This is the Camera Serial Interface where an official Raspberry Pi camera can be attached here.

HDMI: A suitable monitor can be connected to this port. The port carries both audio and video.

USB power: A +5V 2A power supply should be connected to this USB socket to provide power to the raspberry Pi 3.

SD card slot: A micro SD card carrying the operating system must be attached to this slot.

DSI: A suitable display can be connected to this Display Interface.

SOC: This is the Broadcom BCM2837 System On Chip which contains the 1.2GHz 64-bit quad core ARM Cortex-A53 processor.

GPIO: The General Purpose Input-Output port is 40 pin wide.

BCM43438: This chip provides the Wi-Fi and Bluetooth to the Raspberry Pi 3.

2.3 Setting Up the Operating System

The Raspberry Pi 3 is sold in several different formats. Some distributors supply all the necessary adapters, power supply, and even the pre-installed operating system on a micro SD card. The operating system on a micro SD card can also be purchased separately. In this section we shall see how to load the operating system on a micro SD card. In this book the recommended popular Raspbian operating system is used.

If you have purchased your Raspberry Pi 3 with the operating system pre-installed on a micro SD card then you can skip this and the next sections.

There are basically two methods to install the operating system on an SD card: Using the NOOBS, and Installing the image files. Both methods are described in the next sections.

2.3.1 Using NOOBS

The instructions to install the operating system on a blank micro SD card are using the NOOBS are given below. You will need a micro SD card with a capacity of at least 8 GB of memory, although16 GB is recommended for future expansion and installing new applications and programs. You might need a standard size SD card adapter to insert the micro SD card into your computer's card slot.

- Download (ZIP) the current file Image of Raspbian from the following site (see Figure 2.2) to a folder on your PC (e.g. to C:\RPI). It is recommended that first time users download and install the software called NOOBS (**N**ew **O**ut **O**f **B**ox **S**oftware) onto a new 8GB or larger micro SD card. The version at the time of writing this book was 2.4.3:

www.raspberrypi.org/downloads/raspbian

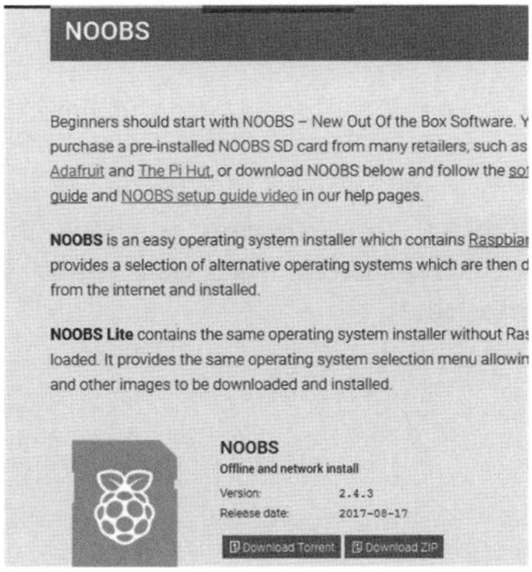

Figure 2.2 Download the NOOBS software

- Install the SD Formatter software from the SD Association's web site (see Figure 2.3). At the time of writing this book the software was called SD_CardFormatter-0500SetupEN.exe:

https://www.sdcard.org/downloads/formatter_4/eula_windows/index.html

Figure 2.3 Install the SD Formatter software

- Insert your SD card into your computer's card socket and make note of the drive letter allocated to it. e.g. **F:** as shown in Figure 2.4

Figure 2.4 Make a note of the drive letter allocated to your SD card

- Start the SD card formatter you have installed and enter the drive letter to format the SD card, select **Quick format** as shown in Figure 2.5 (**be careful to enter the correct drive letter here otherwise you might delete all the files on your computer!**).

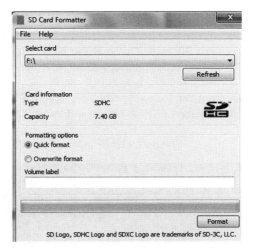

Figure 2.5 Enter the SD card drive letter

- Extract all the files from the folder where you have stored the NOOBS operating system ZIP file.

- Drag all the extracted files and drop them to the newly formatted SD card. All the necessary files will be transferred to the SD card. After copying, part of the contents of the SD card are shown in Figure 2.6

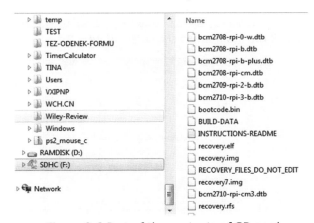

Figure 2.6 Part of the contents of SD card

- Remove the SD card from your computer and install into the Raspberry Pi 3 micro SD card slot.

- Notice that further information about the installation process can be obtained from the following link:

  https://www.raspberrypi.org/learning/software-guide/quickstart/

2.3.2 Installing Image Files on micro SD Card

The Raspbian operating system can also be downloaded as image and copied bit by bit from the downloaded file to the micro SD card. This method has the advantage that it is easier to do compared to the NOOBS method. The instructions are given below.

- Install the Etcher from the following web link to your PC (here it is assumed that you have a Windows based PC), as shown in Figure 2.7:

https://etcher.io/

Figure 2.7 Etcher program

- Click to download the application. The application file at the time or writing this book was called: Etcher-Setup-1.1.2-x64.exe. Drag the file to a folder and double click it to install the program as shown in Figure 2.8.

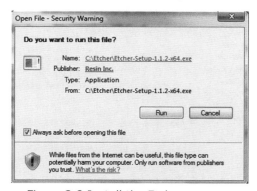

Figure 2.8 Install the Etcher program

- Download the **Raspbian Stretch With Desktop** from the Raspberry Pi web site (see Figure 2.9) by clicking Download Zip:

www.raspberrypi.org/downloads/raspbian

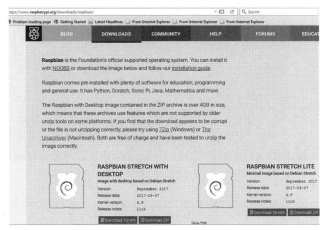

Figure 2.9 Download Raspbian Stretch With Desktop

- Copy the downloaded program to a folder. Right click on file 2017-09-07-raspbian-stretch.zip file (at the time of writing this book) and extract all the files (see Figure 2.10). You should have a file with the extension .img.

Figure 2.10 Extract all the files

- Start the Etcher program by double clicking on it (Figure 2.11). There are three menu options: select image, select drive, and flash.

Figure 2.11 Start the Etcher program

- Click the settings icon at the top right hand corner of the display. You should see some items already ticked. Make sure that the last two items are not ticked (see Figure 2.12). Click Back at the top right hand corner.

Figure 2.12 Etcher settings menu

- Select image and locate the extracted image file and click on it (see Figure 2.13)

Figure 2.13 Select the saved image file

You should see a screen as in Figure 2.14.

Figure 2.14 Image file selected

- Insert a blank at least 8GB micro SD card into your laptop (you may need an adapter). Select the SD card drive as shown in Figure 2.15. In this example a 16GB micro SD card is used.

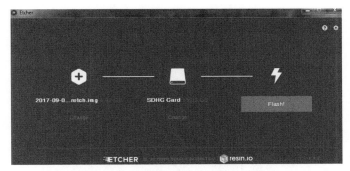

Figure 2.15 Select the SD card dive

- Click Flash to start copying the image to the micro SD card. Wait until it is copied and validated as it may take over several minutes to complete. When finished, remove the card and insert into your Raspberry Pi 3.

2.4 Applying Power to the Raspberry Pi 3

Connect the monitor to the HDMI port, and the keyboard/mouse to the USB data port and the power supply to the USB power port. After a short while you will see the startup menu on the monitor as shown in Figure 2.16. Select the **Raspbian** operating system (recommended) and click the **Install** button (at the top left of the menu). Click **Yes** to confirm to install the **Raspbian** operating system. You should see the message **Raspbian: Extracting filesystem** at the bottom of the monitor. Wait for 5 to 10 few minutes until the operating system has been installed on the SD card (see Figure 2.18). You should see a progress bar at the bottom of the monitor as the installation process continues.

Notice that the author used the **Ultra Mini Keyboard** with built-in mouse as shown in Figure 2.17. This keyboard is connected to the Raspberry Pi 3 via the wireless USB port.

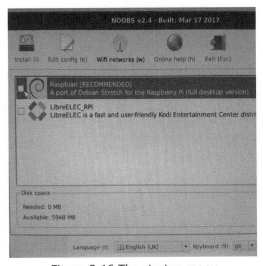

Figure 2.16 The startup menu

Figure 2.17 Mini keyboard/mouse

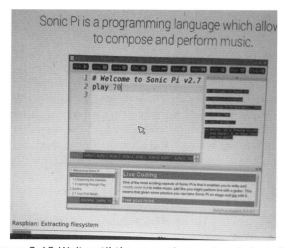

Figure 2.18 Wait until the operating system is installed

At the end of the installation you should restart the Raspberry Pi 3 which will display the GUI screen shown in Figure 2.19 after the restart.

Figure 2.19 Screen after the restart

2.5 Setting Up the Wi-Fi and Remote Access

It is very likely that you will want to access your Raspberry Pi 3 remotely from your desktop or laptop computer. The easiest option here is to enable Wi-Fi on your Pi computer and then access it from your computer using the SSH client protocol. This protocol requires a server and a client. The server is your Pi computer and the client is your desktop or laptop computer. In this section we will see how to enable the Wi-Fi on your Pi computer and how to access it remotely.

Setting Up Wi-Fi

To enable the Wi-Fi on your Pi, the steps are as follows:

- Click on the Wi-Fi icon which is a pair of red crosses at the top right hand side of the screen

- Select your Wi-Fi router from the displayed list (see Figure 2.20)

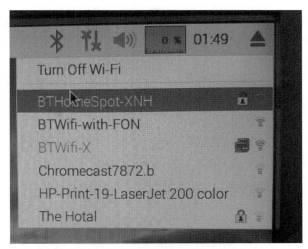

Figure 2.20 Select your Wi-Fi from the list

- Enter the password for your Wi-Fi router

- The WiFi icon should become a typical Wi-Fi image. If you click on the icon now you should see a green tick next to the selected router as shown in Figure 2.21.

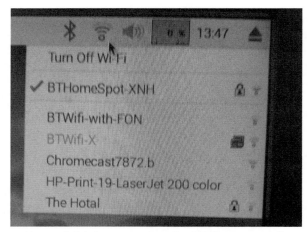

Figure 2.21 Connected to the Wi-Fi successfully

- To see the IP address of your Wi-Fi connection, place the mouse over the Wi-Fi icon as shown in Figure 2.22. In this example the IP address was 192.168.1.84

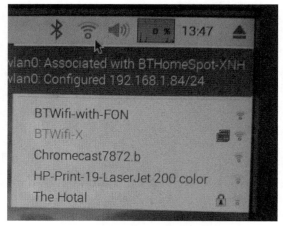

Figure 2.22 IP address of our connection

Remote Access

The program we will be using to access our Raspberry Pi 3 is called **Putty** with the SSH protocol. The steps to download and use Putty are as follows:

- Download Putty from the following link (or search Google for "Download Putty")

    http://www.chiark.greenend.org.uk/~sgtatham/putty/download.html

- For security reasons the SSH protocol is disabled by default on a new operating system. To enable it, click on the **Applications** menu at the top left of the screen, click **Accessories**, and then click **Terminal** (see Figure 2.23)

Figure 2.23 Access the Terminal menu

- You should now be in the Raspberry Pi 3 command prompt. Type:

raspi-config

to go into the configuration menu and select **Interface Options**. Go down to **P2 SSH** and enable SSH as shown in Figure 2.24

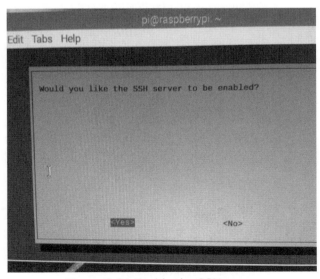

Figure 2.24 Enable the SSH server

- Click <Finish> to exit the configuration menu. You should now be back in the command mode, identified by the prompt:

pi@raspberrypi:~ $

- Putty is a standalone program and there is no need to install it. Simply double click to run it. You should see the Putty startup screen as in Figure 2.25.

Figure 2.25 Putty startup screen

- Make sure that the Connection type is SSH and enter the IP address of your Raspberry Pi 3. Click Open as shown in Figure 2.26.

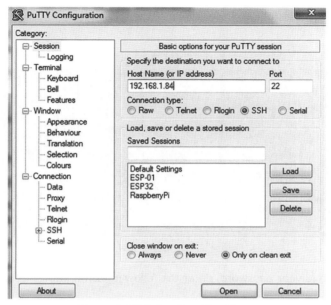

Figure 2.26 Enter the IP address

- The message shown in Figure 2.27 will be displayed on the PC screen the first time you access the Raspberry Pi 3. Click Yes to accept this security alert.

Figure 2.27 Click Yes to accept

- You will then be prompted for the username and password. The default values are:

Username: **pi**
Password: **raspberry**

- After a successful login you should see the Raspberry Pi command prompt as in Figure 2.28.

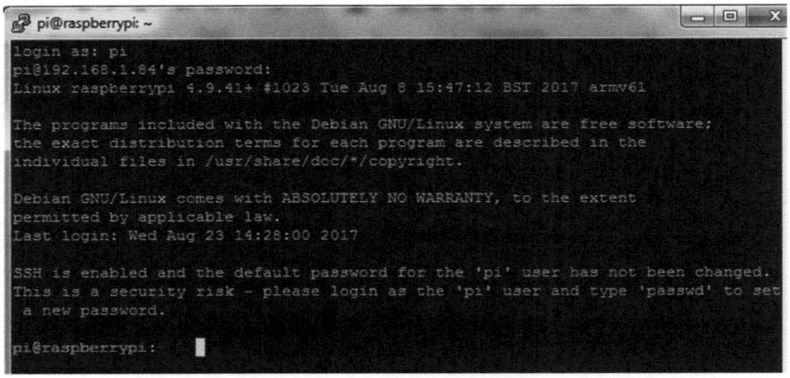

Figure 2.28 Successful login

- To change your password, enter the following command:

   passwd

- To restart the RPi ZW enter the following command:

   sudo reboot

- To shut down the RPi ZW enter the following command. Never shutdown by pulling the power cable as this may result in the corruption or loss of files:

   sudo shutdown –h now

2.6 Shutting Down or Rebooting in GUI Mode

You must always shutdown your Pi computer properly. To shut down while in the GUI mode, follow the steps given below:

- Click Applications menu (top left corner)

- Click Shutdown (see Figure 2.29)

- Click Shutdown (or Reboot as required)

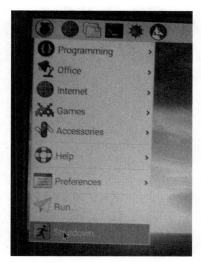

Figure 2.29 Shutdown or reboot in GUI mode

2.7 Remote Access of the Desktop

If you will be using your Raspberry Pi 3 with local keyboard, mouse, and monitor you can skip this section. If on the other hand you want to access your Desktop remotely over the network, you will find that SSH services cannot be used. The easiest and simplest way to access your Desktop remotely from a computer is by installing the VNC (Virtual Network Connection) client and server. The VNC server runs on your Pi and the VNC client runs on your computer. The steps to install and use the VNC are given below:

- Connect to your Pi computer using SSH as explained earlier. Then enter the following command to install a program called TightVNC server on your Pi computer. You will see many lines of messages. Make sure there are no error messages:

  sudo apt-get update
  sudo apt-get install tightvncserver

- Run the VNC server on your Pi computer by entering the following command:

  vncserver :1

- You will be prompted to enter and verify a password. This will be the password you will be using to access the Desktop remotely (see Figure 2.30).

```
update-alternatives: using /usr/bin/tightvncpasswd to provide
 (vncpasswd) in auto mode
Processing triggers for man-db (2.7.6.1-2) ...

Processing triggers for shared-mime-info (1.8-1) ...
Processing triggers for gnome-menus (3.13.3-9) ...
Processing triggers for hicolor-icon-theme (0.15-1) ...
Setting up xfonts-base (1:1.0.4+nmu1) ...
Processing triggers for fontconfig (2.11.0-6.7) ...
pi@raspberrypi:  $ vncserver :1

You will require a password to access your desktops.

Password:
Verify:
Would you like to enter a view-only password (y/n)? n

New 'X' desktop is raspberrypi:1

Creating default startup script /home/pi/.vnc/xstartup
Starting applications specified in /home/pi/.vnc/xstartup
Log file is /home/pi/.vnc/raspberrypi:1.log

pi@raspberrypi:- $
```

Figure 2.30 Enter a password for the VNC server

- The VNC server is now running on your Pi computer. The only command you need to enter on your Pi computer to start the VNC server is:

   vncserver :1

- We must now setup a VNC client on our laptop (or desktop). There are many VNC clients available, but the recommended one which is compatible with TightVNC is the VNC Viewer, which can be downloaded from the following link. Notice that this program is not free of charge, but a 30 day free trial version is available. You should register to get a trial license and then apply this license to the software to use free of charge for 30 days:

   http://www.realvnc.com

- Download the VNC Viewer program into a suitable directory on your computer.

- Double click to install it and enter the required license. Start the **VNC Viewer** Program by double clicking its icon in your desktop. Enter the IP address of your Raspberry Pi 3followed by :1 as shown in Figure 2.31 and click Connect.

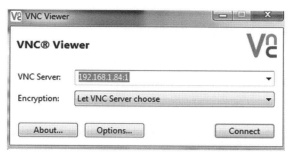

Figure 2.31 Enter the IP address

- Enter the password selected previously. You should now see the Raspberry Pi 3 Desktop displayed on your laptop (or desktop) computer as in Figure 2.32 and you can access all of the Desktop applications remotely.

Figure 2.32 Raspberry Pi 3 Desktop displayed on the laptop

2.8 Enabling Bluetooth

In this section we will see how to enable the Bluetooth on your Raspberry Pi 3 so that it can communicate with your mobile phone. The steps are given below:

- Enable the Bluetooth on your mobile device

- Click on the Bluetooth icon on your Raspberry Pi 3 at the top right hand side, and select **Make Discoverable.** You should see the Bluetooth icon flashing

- Select raspberrypi in the Bluetooth menu on your mobile device

- Accept the pairing request on your Raspberry Pi 3 as shown in Figure 2.33

Figure 2.33 Bluetooth pairing request

- You should now see the message **Connected Successfully** on your Raspberry Pi 3 and you can exchange files between your mobile device and the Pi computer.

2.9 Connecting the Raspberry Pi 3 to a Wired Network

You may want to connect your Raspberry Pi 3 to a network through an Ethernet cable. The steps are as follows:

- **Step 1:** Connect a network cable between your Raspberry Pi 3 and your home network router.

- **Step 2:** Connect keyboard, mouse and monitor to your Pi and power up as normal

- **Step 3:** Login to the system by entering your username and password

- **Step 4:** Providing your network hub supports DHCP (nearly all network routers support DHCP), you will be connected automatically to the network and will be assigned a unique IP address within your network. Note that DHCP assigns IP addresses to newly connected devices.

- **Step 5:** Check to find out the IP address assigned to your Pi by the network router. Enter the following command:

pi@raspberrypi ~$ **sudo ifconfig**

You should see a display similar to the one shown in Figure 2.34.

```
pi@raspberrypi ~ $ sudo ifconfig
eth0      Link encap:Ethernet  HWaddr b8:27:eb:bb:86:0b
          inet addr:192.168.1.108  Bcast:192.168.1.255  Mask:255.255.255.0
          UP BROADCAST RUNNING MULTICAST  MTU:1500  Metric:1
          RX packets:35 errors:0 dropped:0 overruns:0 frame:0
          TX packets:33 errors:0 dropped:0 overruns:0 carrier:0
          collisions:0 txqueuelen:1000
          RX bytes:3244 (3.1 KiB)  TX bytes:3682 (3.5 KiB)

lo        Link encap:Local Loopback
          inet addr:127.0.0.1  Mask:255.0.0.0
          UP LOOPBACK RUNNING  MTU:16436  Metric:1
          RX packets:8 errors:0 dropped:0 overruns:0 frame:0
          TX packets:8 errors:0 dropped:0 overruns:0 carrier:0
          collisions:0 txqueuelen:0
          RX bytes:1104 (1.0 KiB)  TX bytes:1104 (1.0 KiB)

pi@raspberrypi ~ $
```

Figure 2.34 ifconfig display

Note here that we are looking for the line starting with words **inet addr** under **eth0**:

Inet addr: 192.168.1.108 Bcast: 192.168.1.255 Mask: 255.255.255.0

Here, we are interested in the IP address which in this case is 192.168.1.108. We should now be able to connect to the internet or connect to our Pi from anywhere on our network.

Notice that we can also use the following command to find our IP address:

pi@raspberrypi ~$ **hostname –I**
192.168.1.108
pi@raspberrypi ~$

2.9.1 Unable to Connect to a Wired Network

If you find that you are not assigned an IP address the possible causes are:

- Your network cable is faulty
- The network hub does not support DHCP
- Your Pi is not enabled to accept DHCP issued addresses. i.e. it may have been configured for fixed IP addresses

In most cases it is very unlikely that the network cable is faulty. Also, most network hubs support the DHCP protocol. If you are having problems with the network it is possible that your Pi is not configured to accept DHCP issued addresses. The PI is normally configured to accept DHCP addresses but it is possible that you have changed the configuration somehow.

To resolve the wired network connectivity problem follow the steps given below:

- **Step 1:** find out whether or not your Pi is configured for DHCP or fixed IP addresses. Enter the following command:

  pi@raspberrypi ~$ **cat /etc/network/interfaces**

  if your Pi is configured to use the DHCP protocol (which is normally the default configuration), the word **dhcp** should appear at the end of the following line:

  iface eth0 inet dhcp

  if your Pi is configured to use static addresses then you should see the word **static** at the end of the following line:

  iface eth0 inet static

- **Step 2:** To use the DHCP protocol, edit file **interfaces** (e.g. using the **nano** text editor) and change the word **static** to **dhcp**. We shall see in the next chapter how to edit a text file. It is recommended to make a backup copy of the file interfaces before you change it:

> pi@raspberrypi ~$ **sudo cp /etc/network/interfaces /etc/network/int.bac**

You should now re-start your Pi and an IP address will probably be assigned to you.

- **Step 3:** To use static addressing, make sure that the word **static** appears as shown above. If not, edit file **interfaces** and change **dhcp** to **static**

- **Step 4:** You need to edit and add the required unique IP address, subnet mask and gateway addresses to file **interfaces** as in the following example (this example assumes that the required fixed IP address is 192.168.1.20, the subnet mask used in the network is 255.255.255.0, and the gateway address is 192.168.1.1):

> iface eth0 inet static
> address 192.168.1.20
> netmask 255.255.255.0
> gateway 192.168.1.1

Save the changes and exit the editor. If you are using the **nano** editor, exit by pressing Ctrl+X, then enter Y to save the buffer, and enter the filename to write to as **/etc/network/interfaces**.

Re-start your Raspberry Pi 3. The Pi should boot with the chosen IP address.

2.10 Connecting the Raspberry Pi 3 Directly to a PC Without a Monitor
You can still access your Raspberry Pi even without connecting a monitor, keyboard, and a mouse to it.

If you have a network router available then connect your Raspberry Pi and your PC to the router, get the IP address assigned to your Pi by the DHCP server on the router, and then use the SSH protocol under Putty to access your Raspberry Pi from the PC.

If you do not have a network router, monitor, keyboard and a mouse then it is still possible to establish communication with your Raspberry Pi 3. There are two different methods depending on whether or not you have a network hub. Notice that a network hub is a passive device and it does not have DHCP facilities. i.e. a network hub cannot assign IP addresses to a network device.

The steps to establish communication with your raspberry Pi 3 are given below:

- If you have a network hub, just connect your Raspberry Pi 3 and your PC (e.g.

laptop) to the hub using two Ethernet cables as shown in Figure 2.35.

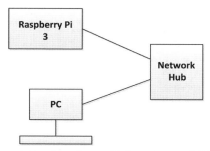

Figure 2.35 Connect the Raspberry Pi 3 and your PC to a network hub

- If you don't have a network hub then you will need a crossed Ethernet network cable. This is a special Ethernet cable where pins 1,3 and 2,6 are crossed. i.e. at one side of the cable, pin 1 and pin 2 are connected to pins 3 and 6 respectively. Similarly, on the other side of the cable again pins 1 and 2 are connected to pins 3 and 6 at the other side of the cable. You should be able to purchase such a cable from many shops selling network parts. Figure 2.36 shows the connection between the raspberry Pi 3 and the PC.

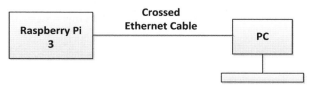

Figure 2.36 Connecting using a crossed Ethernet cable

- With the network hub or with direct connection the Raspberry Pi 3 will not have an IP address assigned since there is no DHCP server available. It is however possible to run a DHCP server program on your PC which can assign an IP address automatically to your Pi. The steps for this are given below:

- First of all, set a fixed IP address on your PC (e.g. 192.168.1.1) as shown in Figure 2.37.

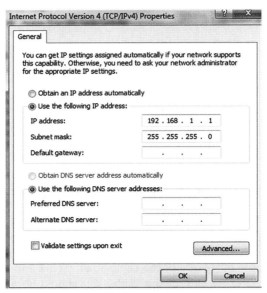

Figure 2.37 Set a fixed IP address on your PC

- Install the DHCP server program at web site www.dhcpserver.de, developed by Uwe A. Ruttkamp. You should have the files as shown in Figure 2.38.

Figure 2.38 Files of the DHCP server on the PC

- Click on the program called dhcpwiz.exe to run the DHCP server. Select the Local Area Connection from the given list. Click Next, skip the next section by clicking Next. In the next screen you will see the address assignment range of the DHCP server. As shown in Figure 2.39 in this example the address range is from 192.168.1.1 to 192.168.1.254. Click Next and then select to Overwrite existing file (Figure 2.40). Click Next and select to run the DHCP server immediately.

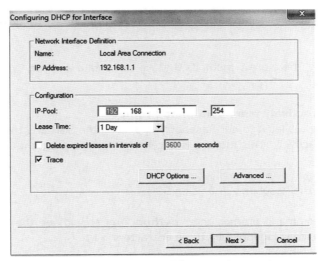

Figure 2.39 DHCP server address assignment range

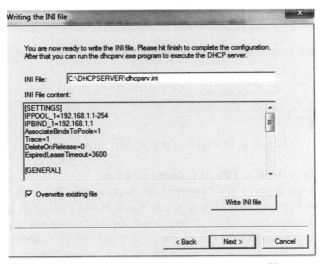

Figure 2.40 Select to overwrite existing file

- Power-up your Raspberry Pi. You should see a small pop-up menu at the bottom right hand corner of your PC with the IP address assigned to your raspberry Pi 3. In this example, the assigned address was 192.168.1.2 (i.e. the next IP address after the PC's IP address)

- You can now use the Putty and the SSH protocol to login to your Raspberry Pi 3.

2.11 Creating and Running a Python Program
We will be programming our Raspberry Pi 3 using the Python programming language. It is worthwhile to look at the creation and running of a simple Python program on our Pi

computer. In this section we will display the message **Hello From Raspberry Pi 3** on our PC screen.

As described below, there are 3 methods that we can create and run Python programs on our Raspberry Pi 3:

Method 1 – Interactively from Command Prompt
In this method, we will login to our Raspberry Pi 3 using the SSH and then create and run our program interactively. This method is excellent for small programs. The steps are as follows:

- Login to the Raspberry Pi 3 using SSH

- At the command prompt enter **python**. You should see the Python command mode which is identified by three characters **>>>**

- Type the program:

print ("Hello From Raspberry Pi 3")

The required text will be displayed interactively on the screen as shown in Figure 2.41

```
pi@raspberrypi:~ $ python
Python 2.7.13 (default, Jan 19 2017, 14:48:08)
[GCC 6.3.0 20170124] on linux2
Type "help", "copyright", "credits" or "license" for more information.
>>> print("Hello From Raspberry Pi 3")
Hello From Raspberry Pi 3
>>> █
```

Figure 2.41 Running a program interactively

Method 2 – Create a Python File in Command Mode
In this method, we will login to our Raspberrry Pi 3 using the SSH as before and then create a Python file. A Python file is simply a text file with the extension **.py**. We can use a text editor, e.g. the **nano** text editor to create our file. In this example a file called **hello.py** is created using the **nano** text editor. Figure 2.42 shows the contents of file hello.py. This figure also shows how to run the file under Python. Notice that the program is run by entering the command:

>>> python hello.py

```
pi@raspberrypi:   $ ls hello.py
hello.py
pi@raspberrypi:   $ cat hello.py
print ("Hello From  Raspberry Pi Zero W")

pi@raspberrypi:   $ python hello.py
Hello From  Raspberry Pi Zero W
pi@raspberrypi:   $ █
```

Figure 2.42 Creating and running a Python file

Method 3 – Create a Python File in GUI mode

In this method, we will login to our Raspberry Pi 3 using the VNC and create and run our program in GUI mode. The steps are given below:

- Click Applications menu

- Click Programming and select Python 2 or Python 3 (see Figure 2.43)

Figure 2.43 Select Python 2 programming

- You should see the Python command mode, identified by characters >>>

- Click **File** and then click **New File** and write your program

- Save the file by giving it a name (e.g. hello2)

- Run the program by clicking **Run** and then **Run Module** as shown in Figure 2.44

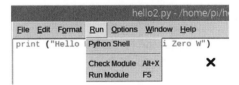

Figure 2.44 Run the program

- A new screen will be shown with the output of the program displayed as in Figure 2.45

```
                              Python 2.7.13 Shell            -
  File  Edit  Shell  Debug  Options  Window  Help
  Python 2.7.13 (default, Jan 19 2017, 14:48:08)
  [GCC 6.3.0 20170124] on linux2
  Type "copyright", "credits" or "license()" for more information.
  >>>
  ======================= RESTART: /home/pi/hello2.py =======================
  Hello From Raspberry Pi Zero W
  >>>
```

Figure 2.45 Output of the program

Which Method ?

The choice of a method depends upon the size and complexity of a program. Small programs can be run interactively without creating a program file. Larger programs can be created as Python files and then they can run either in the command mode or in the GUI mode. In this book, program files are created for all the Python programs.

2.12 The GPIO Library

The GPIO library is called RPi.GPIO and it should already be installed on your Raspberry Pi 3. This library must be included at the beginning of your Python programs if you will be using the GPIO functions. The statement to include this library is:

import RPi.GPIO as GPIO

If you get an error while trying to import the GPIO library then it is possible that the library is not installed. Enter the following commands while in the command mode (identified by the prompt **pi@raspberrypi:~ $**) to install the GPIO library (characters that should be entered by you are in bold):

pi@raspberrypi: ~ $ **sudo apt-get update**
pi@raspberrypi: ~$ **sudo apt-get install python-dev**
pi@raspberrypi: ~$ **sudo apt-get install python-rpi.gpio**

The GPIO provides a number of useful functions. The available functions are given in the next sections

2.12.1 Pin Numbering

There are two ways that we can refer to the GPIO pins. The first is using the BOARD numbering, where the pin numbers on the GPIO connector of the Raspberry Pi 3 are used. Enter the following statement to use the BOARD method:

GPIO.setmode(GPIO.BOARD)

The second numbering system, also known as the BCM method is the preferred method and it uses the channel numbers allocated to the pins. This method requires that you know which channel number refers to which pin on the board. In this book we shall be using this second method. Enter the following statement to use the BCM method:

GPIO.setmode(GPIO.BCM)

The GPIO is a 40 pin header, mounted at one side of the board. Appendix A shows the Raspberry Pi 3 GPIO pin configuration.

2.12.2 Channel (I/O port pin) Configuration

Input Configuration

You need to configure the channels (or port pins) you are using whether they are input or output channels. The following statement is used to configure a channel as an input. Here, channel refers to the channel number based on the **setmode** statement above:

GPIO.setup(channel, GPIO.IN)

When there is nothing connected to an input pin, the data at this input is not defined. We can specify additional parameters with the input configuration statement to connect pull-up or pull-down resistors by software to an input pin. The required statements are:
For pull-down:

GPIO.setup(channel, GPIO.IN, pull_up_down=GPIO.PUD_DOWN)

For pull-up:

GPIO.setup(channel, GPIO.IN, pull_up_down=GPIO.PUD_UP)

We can detect an edge change of an input signal at an input pin. Edge change is when the signal changes from LOW to HIGH (rising edge), or from HIGH to LOW (falling edge). For example, pressing a push-button switch can cause an edge change at the input of a pin. The following statements can be used to wait for an edge of the input signal. These are blocking functions. i.e. the program will wait until the specified edge is detected at the input signal. For example, if this is a push-button, the program will wait until the button is pressed:

To wait for a rising edge:

GPIO.wait_for_edge(channel, GPIO.RISING)

To wait for a falling edge:

GPIO.wait_for_edge(channel, GPIO.FALLING)

We can also wait until either a rising or a falling edge is detected by using the following statement:

GPIO.wait_for_edge(channel, GPIO.BOTH)

We can use event detection function with an input pin. This way, we can execute the event detection code whenever an event is detected. Events can be rising edge, falling edge, or change in either edge of the signal. Event detection is usually used in loops where we can check for the event while executing other code.

For example, to add rising event detection to an input pin:

GPIO.add_event_detect(channel, GPIO.RISING)

We can check whether or not the event occurred by the following statement:

If GPIO.event_detected(channel):
....
....

Event detection can be removed by the following statement:

GPIO.remove_event_detect(channel)

We can also use interrupt facilities (or callbacks) to detect events. Here, the event is handled inside a user function. The main program carries on its usual duties and as soon as the event occurs the program stops whatever it is doing and jumps to the event handling function. For example, the following statement can be used to add interrupt based event handling to our programs on rising edge of an input signal. In this example, the event handling code is the function named **MyHandler**:

GPIO.add_event_detect(channel, GPIO.RISING, callback=MyHandler)
....
....

def MyHandler(channel):
....
....

We can add more than one interrupt by using the add_event_callback function. Here the callback functions are executed sequentially:

GPIO.add_event_detect(channel, GPIO.RISING)
GPIO.add_event_callback(channel, MyHandler1)
GPIO.add_event_callback(channel, MyHandler2)
....
....

def MyHandler1(channel):
....
....

def MyHandler2(channel):

....
....

When we use mechanical switches in our projects we get what is known as the switch bouncing problem. This occurs as the contacts of the switch bounce many times until they settle to their final state. Switch bouncing could generate several pulses before it settles down. We can avoid switch bouncing problems in hardware or software. GPIO library provides a parameter called bouncetime that can be used to eliminate the switch bouncing problem. An example use of this parameter is shown below where the switch bounce time is assumed to be 10ms:

GPIO.add_event_detect(channel,GPIO=RISING,callback=MyHandler, bouncetime=10)

We can also use the callback statement to specify the switch bouncing time as@

GPIO.add_event_callback(channel, MyHandler, bouncetime=10)

To read the state of an input pin we can use the following statement:

GPIO.input(channel)

Output Configuration
The following statement is used to configure a channel as an output. Here, channel refers to the port number based on the **setmode** statement described earlier:

GPIO.setup(channel, GPIO.OUT)

We can specify a value for an output pin during its setup. For example, we can configure a channel as output and at the same time set its value to logic HIGH (+3.3V):

GPIO.setup(channel, GPIO.OUT, initial=GPIO.HIGH)

To send data to an output port pin we can use the following statement:

GPIO.output(channel, value)

Where value can be 0 (or GPIO.LOW, or False), or 1 (or GPIO.HIGH, or True)

At the end of the program we should return all the used resources to the operating system. This is done by including the following statement at the end of our program:

GPIO.cleanup()

2.13 Summary

In this Chapter we have looked at the names and functions of the main parts on the Raspberry Pi 3 board. Additionally, we have seen how to install the Raspbian operating system on a micro SD card so that it can be plugged-in and used on our Raspberry Pi 3. We have also seen how to access the Raspberry Pi 3 remotely over a Wi-Fi link and also how to enable the Bluetooth connectivity. In the last sections of this Chapter we have seen how to use the general purpose input-output ports of the Raspberry Pi 3.

In the next chapter we shall be looking at some of the important Linux commands that can be entered from the Raspberry Pi command mode.

CHAPTER 3 • USING THE COMMAND LINE

3.1 Overview
Raspberry Pi is based on a version of the Linux operating system. Linux is one of the most popular operating systems in use today. Linux is very similar to other operating systems, such as Windows and UNIX. Linux is an Open operating system based on UNIX, and has been developed collaboratively by many companies since 1991. In general, Linux is harder to manage than some other operating systems like Windows, but offers more flexibility and configuration options. There are several popular versions of the Linux operating system such as Debian, Ubuntu, Red Hat, Fedora and so on.

Linux instructions are text-based. In this chapter we shall be looking at some of the useful Linux commands and see how you can manage your Raspberry Pi using these commands.

When you apply power to your Raspberry Pi, the Linux command line (or the Linux shell) is the first thing you see and it is where you can enter operating system commands.

3.2 The Command Prompt
After you login to Raspberry Pi, you see the following prompt displayed where the system waits for you to enter a command:

pi@raspberrypi ~$

Here, **pi** is the name of the user who is logged in.

raspberrypi is the name of the computer, used to identify it when connecting over the network.

~ character indicates that you are currently in your default directory.
$ character indicates that you are a normal user (not a privileged super-user)

3.3 Useful Linux Commands
In this section we shall be looking at some of the useful Linux commands where examples will be given for each command. **In this chapter, commands entered by the user are shown in bold for clarity**. Also, it is important to remind you that all the commands must be terminated by the Enter key.

3.3.1 System and User Information
These commands are useful as they tell us information about the system. Command **cat / proc/cpuinfo** displays information about the processor (command cat displays the contents of a file. In this example, the contents of file /proc/cpuinfo is displayed). Since there are 4 cores in the Raspberry Pi 3, the display is in 4 sections. Figure 3.1 shows an example display, where only part of the display is shown here.

```
pi@raspberrypi:~ $ cat /proc/cpuinfo
processor       : 0
model name      : ARMv7 Processor rev 4 (v7l)
BogoMIPS        : 38.40
Features        : half thumb fastmult vfp edsp neon vfpv3 tls vfpv4 idiva idivt
vfpd32 lpae evtstrm crc32
CPU implementer : 0x41
CPU architecture: 7
CPU variant     : 0x0
CPU part        : 0xd03
CPU revision    : 4

processor       : 1
model name      : ARMv7 Processor rev 4 (v7l)
BogoMIPS        : 38.40
Features        : half thumb fastmult vfp edsp neon vfpv3 tls vfpv4 idiva idivt
vfpd32 lpae evtstrm crc32
CPU implementer : 0x41
CPU architecture: 7
CPU variant     : 0x0
CPU part        : 0xd03
CPU revision    : 4

processor       : 2
```

Figure 3.1 Command: cat /proc/cpuinfo

Command **uname −s** displays the operating system Kernel name, which is Linux. Command **uname −a** displays complete detailed information about the Kernel and the operating system. An example is shown in Figure 3.2.

```
pi@raspberrypi:~ $
pi@raspberrypi:~ $ uname -s
Linux
pi@raspberrypi:~ $ uname -a
Linux raspberrypi 4.9.41-v7+ #1023 SMP Tue Aug 8 16:00:15 BST 2017 armv7l GNU/Li
nux
pi@raspberrypi:~ $ ▐
```

Figure 3.2 Commands: uname −s and uname − a

Command **cat /proc/meminfo** displays information about the memory on your Pi. Information such as the total memory and free memory at the time of issuing the command are displayed. Figure 3.3 shows an example, where only part of the display is shown here.

```
pi@raspberrypi:~ $ cat /proc/meminfo
MemTotal:           945512 kB
MemFree:            677372 kB
MemAvailable:       796884 kB
Buffers:             22384 kB
Cached:             145152 kB
SwapCached:              0 kB
Active:             134172 kB
Inactive:           100596 kB
Active(anon):        67500 kB
Inactive(anon):       7480 kB
Active(file):        66672 kB
Inactive(file):      93116 kB
Unevictable:             0 kB
Mlocked:                 0 kB
SwapTotal:          102396 kB
SwapFree:           102396 kB
Dirty:                   4 kB
Writeback:               0 kB
AnonPages:           67240 kB
Mapped:              76040 kB
Shmem:                7744 kB
Slab:                19528 kB
SReclaimable:         9560 kB
```

Figure 3.3 Command: cat /proc/meminfo

Command **whoami** displays the name of the current user. Figure 3.4 shows that the current user is pi.

```
pi@raspberrypi:~ $ whoami
pi
pi@raspberrypi:~ $ ▮
```

Figure 3.4 Command: whoami

A new user can be added to our Raspberry Pi using the command **useradd**. In the example in Figure 3.5, user called Johnson is added. A password for the new user can be added using the **passwd** command followed by the username. In Figure 3.5, the password for user Johnson is set to mypassword (not displayed for security reasons). Notice that both the **useradd** and **passwd** are privileged commands and the keyword **sudo** must be entered before these commands. Notice that the –m option creates a home directory for the new user.

```
pi@raspberrypi:~ $ sudo useradd -m Johnson
pi@raspberrypi:~ $ sudo passwd Johnson
Enter new UNIX password:
Retype new UNIX password:
passwd: password updated successfully
pi@raspberrypi:~ $ ▮
```

Figure 3.5 Commands: useradd and passwd

We can login to the new user account by specifying the username and the password as shown in Figure 3.6. You can type command **exit** to logout from the new account.

```
pi@raspberrypi:~ $ su Johnson
Password:
$ ▮
```

Figure 3.6 Logging in to a new account

3.3.2 The Raspberry Pi Directory Structure

The Raspberry Pi directory structure consists of a single root directory, with directories and subdirectories under the root. Different types of operating system programs and application programs are stored in different directories and subdirectories.

Figure 3.1 shows part of the Raspberry Pi directory structure. Notice that the root directory is identified by the "**/**" symbol. Under the root we have directories named such as bin, boot, dev, etc, home, lib, lost+found, media, mnt, opt, proc, and many more. The important directory as far as the users are concerned is the **home** directory. The **home** directory contains subdirectories for each user of the system. In the example in Figure 3.7, **pi** is the subdirectory for user **pi**. In a new system this subdirectory contains two subdirectories called **Desktop** and **python_games**.

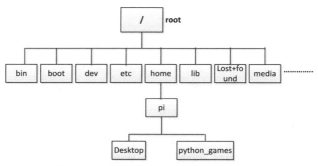

Figure 3.7 Raspberry Pi directory structure (only part of it is shown)

Some useful directory commands are given below. Command **pwd** displays the user home directory:

> pi@raspberrypi ~$ **pwd**
> /home/pi
> pi@raspberry ~$

To show the directory structure, enter the command **ls /**:

> pi@raspberrypi ~$ **ls /**
> bin boot dev etc home lib lost+found media mnt opt proc root run sbin selinux srv
> sys tmp usr var
> pi@raspberrypi ~$

To show the subdirectories and files in our working directory, enter **ls**:

> pi@raspberrypi ~$ **ls**
> Desktop ocr_pi.png python_games
> pi@raspberrypi ~$

Notice that the subdirectories are displayed in blue colour. There are two subdirectories called **Desktop** and **python_games**. There is also a file in the working directory called **ocr_pi.png** which is displayed in pink colour.

The **ls** command can take a number of arguments. Some examples are given below.

To display the subdirectories and files in a single row:

> pi@raspberrypi ~$ **ls -1**
> Desktop
> myfiles
> ocr_pi.png
> python_games
> pi@raspberrypi ~$

to display the file type, enter the following command. Note that directories have a "/" after their names, and executable files have a "*" character after their names:

> pi@raspberrypi ~$ **ls −F**
> Desktop/ myfiles/ ocr_pi.png python_games/
> pi@raspberrypi ~$

to list the results, separated by commas:

> pi@raspberrypi ~$ **ls −m**
> Desktop, myfiles, ocr_pi.png, python_games
> pi@raspberrypi ~$

we can mix the arguments as in the following example:

> pi@raspberrypi ~$ **ls −m −F**
> Desktop/, myfiles/, ocr_pi.png, python_games/
> pi@raspberrypi ~$

Subdirectories are created using command **mkdir** followed by the name of the subdirectory. In the following example, subdirectory myfiles is created in our working directory:

> pi@raspberrypi ~$ **mkdir myfiles**
> pi@raspberrypi ~$ **ls**
> Desktop myfiles ocr_pi.png python_games
> pi@raspberrypi ~$

File Permissions

One of the important arguments used with the **ls** command is "-l" (lower case letter l) which displays the file permissions, file sizes, and when they were last modified. In the example below, each line relates to one directory or file. Reading from right to left, the name of the directory or the file is on the right hand side. The date the directory or file was created is on the left hand side of its name. Next comes the size, given in bytes. For example, file **mytestfile.txt** consists of 23 bytes. The characters at the beginning of each line are about the permissions. i.e. who is allowed to use or modify the file or the directory.

The permissions are divided into 3 categories:

- What the user (or owner, or creator) can do – called USER
- What the group owner (people in the same group) can do - GROUP
- What everyone else can do – called WORLD

The first word **pi** in the example in Figure 3.8 shows who the user of the file (or directory) is, and the second word **pi** shows the group name that owns the file. In this example, both the user and the group names are **pi**.

```
drwxr-xr-x  2 pi pi 4096 Aug 16 01:41 Music
-rw-r--r--  1 pi pi   23 Sep 23 12:55 mytestfile.txt
drwxr-xr-x  2 pi pi 4096 Aug 16 01:41 Pictures
drwxr-xr-x  2 pi pi 4096 Aug 16 01:41 Public
drwxr-xr-x  2 pi pi 4096 Aug 16 01:11 python_games
```

Figure 3.8 File permissions example

The permissions can be analysed by breaking down the characters into four chunks for: File type, User, Group, World. The first character for a file is "-" and for a directory it is "d". Next comes the permissions for the User, Group and World. The permissions are as follows:

- Read permission (r): the permission to open and read a file or to list a directory
- Write permission (w): the permission to modify a file, or to delete or create a file in a directory
- Execute permission (x): the permission to execute the file (applies to executable files), or to enter a directory

The three letters **rwx** are used as a group and if there is no permission assigned then a "-" character is used.

As an example, considering the **Music** directory, we have the following permission codes:

drwxr-xr-x which translates to:

d: it is a directory
rwx: user (owner) can read, write, and execute
r-x: group can read and execute, but cannot write (e.g. create or delete)
r-x: world (everyone else) can read and execute, but cannot write

as another example, let's look at the permissions for file **mytestfile.txt**:

-rw-r--r--   which translates to:

-:   it is a file
rw-:   user (owner) can read and write, but cannot execute (this is not an exe-cutable file)
r--:   group can only read it, they cannot modify, delete, or execute the file
r--:   everyone else (world) can only read it, they cannot modify, delete, or execute the file

The **chmod** command is used to change the file permissions. Before going into details of how to change the permissions, let us look and see what arguments are available in **chmod** for changing the file permissions.

The available arguments for changing file permissions are given below. We can use these arguments to add/remove permissions or to explicitly set permissions. It is important to realize that if we explicitly set permissions then any unspecified permissions in the command will be revoked:

u:	user (or owner)
g:	group
o:	other (world)
a:	all
+:	add
-:	remove
=:	set
r:	read
w:	write
x:	execute

To change the permissions of a file we type the **chmod** command, followed by one of the letters u,g,o,or a to select the people, followed by the +- or = to select the type of change, and finally followed by the filename. An example is given below. In this example, file **mytestfile.txt** has the user read and write permissions. We will be changing the permissions so that the user does not have read permission on this file:

> pi@raspberrypi ~$ **chmod u-r mytestfile.txt**
> pi@raspberrypi ~$ **ls –lh**

The result is shown in Figure 3.9.

```
drwxr-xr-x  2 pi pi 4.0K Aug 16 01:41 Music
--w-r--r--  1 pi pi   23 Sep 23 12:55 mytestfile.txt
drwxr-xr-x  2 pi pi 4.0K Aug 16 01:41 Pictures
drwxr-xr-x  2 pi pi 4.0K Aug 16 01:41 Public
drwxr-xr-x  2 pi pi 4.0K Aug 16 01:11 python games
```

*Figure 3.9 File permissions of **mytestfile.txt***

Notice that if we now try to display the contents of file **mytestfile.txt** using the **cat** command we will get an error message:

> pi@raspberrypi ~$ **cat mytestfile.txt**
> cat: lin.dat: Permission denied
> pi@raspberrypi ~$

All the permissions can be removed from a file by the following command:

> pi@raspberrypi ~$ **chmod a= mytestfile.txt**

Figure 3.10 shows the new permissions of file mytestfile.txt.

```
drwxr-xr-x  2 pi pi 4.0K Aug 16 01:41 Music
----------  1 pi pi   23 Sep 23 12:55 mytestfile.txt
drwxr-xr-x  2 pi pi 4.0K Aug 16 01:41 Pictures
drwxr-xr-x  2 pi pi 4.0K Aug 16 01:41 Public
drwxr-xr-x  2 pi pi 4.0K Aug 16 01:11 python_games
```

*Figure 3.10 New permissions of file **mytestfile.txt***

In the following example, **rwx** user permissions are given to file **mytestfile.txt**:

> pi@raspberrypi ~$ **chmod u+rwx mytestfile.txt**

Figure 3.11 shows the new permissions of file mytestfile.txt.

```
drwxr-xr-x  2 pi pi 4.0K Aug 16 01:41 Music
-rwx------  1 pi pi   23 Sep 23 12:55 mytestfile.txt
drwxr-xr-x  2 pi pi 4.0K Aug 16 01:41 Pictures
drwxr-xr-x  2 pi pi 4.0K Aug 16 01:41 Public
drwxr-xr-x  2 pi pi 4.0K Aug 16 01:11 python_games
```

*Figure 3.11 New permissions of file **mytestfile.txt***

To change our working directory the command **cd** is used. In the following example we change our working directory to **Music**:

> pi@raspberrypi ~$ **cd /home/pi/Music**
> pi@raspberrypi ~/Music $

to go up one directory level, i.e. to our default working directory:

> pi@raspberrypi ~/Music $ **cd..**
> pi@raspberrypi ~$

to change our working directory to **Music**, we can also enter the command:

> pi@raspberrypi ~$ **cd ~/Music**
> pi@raspberrypi ~/myfiles $

to go back to the default working directory, we can enter:

> pi@raspberrypi ~/Music $ **cd ~**
> pi@raspberrypi ~$

to find out more information about a file we can use the file command. For example:

> pi@raspberrypi ~$ **file mytestfiile.txt**
> mytestfile.txt: ASCII text
> pi@raspberrypi ~$

the **−R** argument of command **ls** lists all the files in all the subdirectories of the current working directory. An example is given below. Notice here in Figure 3.12 there are no files in subdirectory **Music** (notice that your listing may be different). Only part of the display is shown here.

```
./Downloads:

./Music:

./Pictures:

./Public:

./python_games:
4row_arrow.png            gem4.png              pentomino.py
4row_black.png            gem5.png              pinkgirl.png
4row_board.png            gem6.png              Plain_Block.png
4row_computerwinner.png   gem7.png              princess.png
4row_humanwinner.png      gemgem.py             RedSelector.png
4row_red.png              grass1.png            Rock.png
4row_tie.png              grass2.png            Selector.png
```

*Figure 3.12 Command: **ls −R***

to display information on how to use a command, we can use the **man** command. As an example, to get help on using the **mkdir** command:

pi@raspberrypi ~$ **man mkdir**
MKDIR(1)

NAME
      Mkdir – make directories

SYNOPSIS
      Mkir [OPTION]...DIRECTORY...

DESCRIPTION
      Create the DIRECTORY(ies), if they do not already exist.

      Mandatory arguments to long options are mandatory for short options

    -m, --mode=MODE
      Set file mode (as in chmod), not a=rwx – umask

Enter Cntrl+Z to exit from the man display.

Help
The **man** command usually gives several pages of information on how to use a command. We can type **q** to exit the **man** command and return to the operating system prompt.

The less command can be used to display a long listing one page at a time. Using the up and down arrow keys we can move between pages. An example is given below. Type **q** to exit:

> pi@raspberrypi ~$ **man ls | less**
> <display of help on using the ls command>
> pi@raspberrypi ~$

Date, Time, and Calendar

To display the current date and time the **date** command is used. Similarly, the cal command displays the current calendar. Figure 3.13 shows an example.

```
--
pi@raspberrypi:~ $ date
Sat 23 Sep 13:20:28 UTC 2017
pi@raspberrypi:~ $ cal
    September 2017
Su Mo Tu We Th Fr Sa
                1   2
 3  4  5  6  7  8  9
10 11 12 13 14 15 16
17 18 19 20 21 22 23
24 25 26 27 28 29 30

pi@raspberrypi:~ $ █
```

*Figure 3.13 Commands: **date** and **cal***

Copying a File

To make copy of a file, use the command cp. In the following example, a copy of file mytestfile.txt is made and the new file is given the name test.txt:

> pi@raspberrypi ~$ **cp mytestfile.txt test.txt**
> pi@raspberrypi ~$

Wildcards

We can use wildcard characters to select multiple files with similar characteristics. e.g. files having the same file-extension names. The "*" character is used to match any number of characters. Similarly, the "?" character is used to match any single character. In the example below all the files with extensions ".png" are listed:

> pi@raspberrypi ~$ **ls *.txt**
> mytestfile.txt   test.txt
> pi@raspberrypi ~$

The wildcard characters [a-z] can be used to match any single character in the specified character range. An example is given below which matches any files that start with letters o, p, q, r, s, and t, and with the ".txt" extension:

> pi@raspberrypi ~$ **ls [o-t]*.txt**
> test.txt
> pi@raspberrypi ~$

Renaming a File

you can rename a file using the **mv** command. In the example below, the name of file **test. txt** is changed to **test2.txt**:

```
pi@raspberrypi ~$ mv test.txt test2.txt
pi@raspberrypi ~$
```

Deleting a File

The command **rm** can be used to remove (delete) a file. In the example below file **test2. txt** is deleted:

```
pi@raspberrypi ~$ rm test2.txt
pi@raspberrypi ~$
```

the argument **−v** can be used to display a message when a file is removed. Also, the **−i** argument asks for confirmation before a file is removed. In general the two arguments are used together as **−vi**. An example is given below:

```
pi@raspberrypi ~$ rm −vi test2.txt
rm: remove regular file 'test2.txt'? y
removed 'test2.txt'
pi@raspberrypi ~$
```

Removing a Directory

A directory can be removed using the **rmdir** command:

```
pi@raspberrypi ~$ rmdir Music
pi@raspberrypi ~$
```

Re-directing the Output

The greater sign > can be used to re-direct the output of a command to a file. For example, we can re-direct the output of the **ls** command to a file called **lstest.txt**:

```
pi@raspberrypi ~$ ls > lstest.txt
pi@raspberrypi ~$
```

The **cat** command can be used to display the contents of a file:

```
pi@raspberrypi ~$ cat mytestfile.txt
This is a file
This is line 2
pi@raspberrypi ~$
```

Using two greater signs **>>** adds to the end of a file. An example is given in Figure 3.14.

```
pi@raspberrypi:~ $ cat mytestfile.txt
this is a file
line 2

pi@raspberrypi:~ $ date >> mytestfile.txt
pi@raspberrypi:~ $ cat mytestfile.txt
this is a file
line 2

Sat 23 Sep 14:03:33 UTC 2017
pi@raspberrypi:~ $ ▮
```

Figure 3.14 Re-directing the output

Writing to the Screen or to a File

The **echo** command can be used to write to the screen. It can be used to perform simple mathematical operations if the numbers and the operation are enclosed in two brackets, preceded by a $ character:

> pi@raspberrypi ~$ **echo $((5*6))**
> 30
> pi@raspberrypi ~$

The echo command can also be used to write a line of text to a file. An example is shown below:

> pi@raspberrypi ~$ **echo a line of text > lin.dat**
> pi@raspberrypi ~$ **cat lin.dat**
> a line of text
> pi@raspberrypi ~$

Matching a String

The grep command can be used to match a string in a file. An example is given below assuming that the file lin.dat contains sting a line of text. Notice that the matched word is shown in bold:

> pi@raspberrypi ~$ **grep line lin.dat**
> a **line** of text
> pi@raspberrypi ~$

Head and Tail Commands

The head command can be used to display the first 10 lines of a file. The format of this command is as follows:

> pi@raspberrypi ~$ **head mytestfile.txt**
> ....
> ....
> pi@raspberrypi ~$

Similarly, the tail command is used to display the last 10 lines of a file. The format of this command is as follows:

> pi@raspberrypi ~$ **tail mytestfile.txt**
> ....
> ....
> pi@raspberrypi ~$

Super User Commands
Some of the commands are privileged and only the authorized persons can use them. Inserting the word **sudo** at the beginning of a command gives us the authority to use the command without having to login as an authorized user.

What Software is Installed on My Raspberry Pi
To find out what software is installed on your Raspberry Pi, enter the following command. You should get several pages of display:

> pi@raspberrypi ~$ **dpkg −l**
> ....
> ....
> pi@raspberrypi ~$

We can also find out if a certain software package is already installed on our computer. An example is given below which checks whether or not software called **xpdf** (PDF reader) is installed. In this example **xpdf** is installed and the details of this software are displayed:

> pi@raspberrypi ~$ **dpkg --s xpdf**
> Package: xpdf
> Status: install ok installed
> Priority: optional
> Section: text
> Installed-Size: 395
> ....
> ....
> pi@raspberrypi ~$

If the software is not installed we get a message similar to the following (assuming we are checking to see if a software package called **bbgd** is installed):

> pi@raspberrypi ~$ **dpkg −s bbgd**
> dpkg-query: package 'bbgd' is not installed and no information is available
> ....
> ....
> pi@raspberrypi ~$

3.3.3 Resource Monitoring on Raspberry Pi

System monitoring is an important topic for managing usage of your Raspberry Pi. One of the most useful system monitoring commands is the top, which displays the current usage of system resources and displays which processes are running and how much memory and CPU time they are consuming.

Figure 3.15 shows a typical system resource display obtained by entering the following command (Enter Ctrl+Z to exit):

> pi@raspberrypi ~$ **top**
> pi@raspberrypi ~$

```
top - 14:10:56 up  1:51,   3 users,   load average: 0.00, 0.00, 0.00
Tasks: 156 total,    1 running, 151 sleeping,   4 stopped,   0 zombie
%Cpu(s):   0.2 us,   0.2 sy,   0.0 ni, 99.6 id,   0.0 wa,   0.0 hi,   0.0 si,   0.0 st
KiB Mem :    945512 total,    661656 free,    93608 used,    190248 buff/cache
KiB Swap:    102396 total,    102396 free,        0 used.    793940 avail Mem

  PID USER      PR  NI    VIRT    RES    SHR S  %CPU %MEM     TIME+ COMMAND
 1155 pi        20   0    8104   3204   2732 R   1.7  0.3   0:00.13 top
  938 pi        20   0   11656   4092   3324 S   0.3  0.4   0:00.52 sshd
    1 root      20   0   27008   5964   4840 S   0.0  0.6   0:02.59 systemd
    2 root      20   0       0      0      0 S   0.0  0.0   0:00.01 kthreadd
    3 root      20   0       0      0      0 S   0.0  0.0   0:00.05 ksoftirqd/0
    5 root       0 -20       0      0      0 S   0.0  0.0   0:00.00 kworker/0:+
    7 root      20   0       0      0      0 S   0.0  0.0   0:00.84 rcu_sched
    8 root      20   0       0      0      0 S   0.0  0.0   0:00.00 rcu_bh
    9 root      rt   0       0      0      0 S   0.0  0.0   0:00.00 migration/0
   10 root       0 -20       0      0      0 S   0.0  0.0   0:00.00 lru-add-dr+
   11 root      20   0       0      0      0 S   0.0  0.0   0:00.00 cpuhp/0
   12 root      20   0       0      0      0 S   0.0  0.0   0:00.00 cpuhp/1
   13 root      rt   0       0      0      0 S   0.0  0.0   0:00.00 migration/1
   14 root      20   0       0      0      0 S   0.0  0.0   0:00.01 ksoftirqd/1
   16 root       0 -20       0      0      0 S   0.0  0.0   0:00.00 kworker/1:+
   17 root      20   0       0      0      0 S   0.0  0.0   0:00.00 cpuhp/2
   18 root      rt   0       0      0      0 S   0.0  0.0   0:00.00 migration/2
```

Figure 3.15 Typical system resource display

Some of the important points in Figure 3.15 are summarized below (for lines 1 to 5 of the display):

- There are total of 156 processes in the system
- Currently only one process is running, 151 processes are sleeping, and 4 processes are stopped
- The percentage CPU utilization is 0.1us for user applications (us)
- The percentage CPU utilization for system applications is 0.3 (sy)
- There are no processes requiring more or less priority (ni)
- 99.6% of the time the CPU is idle (id)
- There are no processes waiting for I/O completion (wa)
- There are no processes waiting for hardware interrupts (hi)
- There are no processes waiting for software interrupts (si)
- There is no time reserved for a hypervisor (st)
- The total usable memory is 945512 bytes, of which 93596 bytes are in use, 661656 bytes are free, and 190260 bytes are used by buffers/cache
- Line 5 displays the swap space usage

The process table gives the following information for all the processes loaded to the system:

- PID: the process ID number
- USER: owner of the process
- PR: priority of the process
- NI: the nice value of the process
- VIRT: the amount of virtual memory used by the process
- RES: size of the resident memory
- SHR: shared memory the process is using
- S: process status (sleeping, running,, zombie)
- %CPU: the percentage of CPU consumed
- %MEM: percentage of RAM used
- TIME+: total CPU time the task used
- COMMAND: The actual name of the command

The **ps** command can be used to list all the processes used by the current user. An example is shown in Figure 3.16.

```
pi@raspberrypi:~ $ ps
  PID TTY          TIME CMD
  941 pts/0    00:00:00 bash
 1060 pts/0    00:00:00 man
 1073 pts/0    00:00:00 pager
 1079 pts/0    00:00:00 man
 1092 pts/0    00:00:00 pager
 1155 pts/0    00:00:01 top
 1181 pts/0    00:00:00 ps
pi@raspberrypi:~ $ 
```

*Figure 3.16 Command: **ps***

the command **ps −ef** gives a lot more information about the processes running in the system.

Killing a Process

There are many options for killing (or stopping) a process. A process can be killed by specifying its PID and using the following command:

pi@raspberrypi ~$ **kill -9 <PID>**

Disk Usage

The disk free command **df** can be used to display the disk usage statistics. An example is shown in Figure 3.17. option **−h** displays in human readable form.

```
pi@raspberrypi:~ $ sudo df -h
Filesystem        Size  Used Avail Use% Mounted on
/dev/root         5.6G  4.2G  1.1G  81% /
devtmpfs          458M     0  458M   0% /dev
tmpfs             462M     0  462M   0% /dev/shm
tmpfs             462M  6.2M  456M   2% /run
tmpfs             5.0M  4.0K  5.0M   1% /run/lock
tmpfs             462M     0  462M   0% /sys/fs/cgroup
/dev/mmcblk0p6     68M   21M   47M  31% /boot
tmpfs              93M  4.0K   93M   1% /run/user/1000
/dev/mmcblk0p5     30M  398K   28M   2% /media/pi/SETTINGS11
pi@raspberrypi:~ $
```

*Figure 3.17 Command: **df***

3.3.4 Shutting Down

Although you can disconnect the power supply from your Raspberry Pi when you finish working with it, it is not recommended since there are many processes running on the system and it is possible to corrupt the file system. It is much better to shut down the system in an orderly manner.

The following command will stop all the processes and make the file system safe and then turn off the system safely:

pi@raspberrypi ~$ **sudo halt**

the following command stops and then re-starts the system:

pi@raspberrypi ~$ **sudo reboot**

the system can also be shut down and then re-started after a time by entering the following command. Optionally, a shut down message can be displayed if desired:

pi@raspberrypi ~$ **shutdown –r <time> <message>**

3.4 Summary

This Chapter has described the use of some of the important Linux commands. You should be able to get further information on each command and other Linux commands from the internet and from other books on Raspberry Pi and Linux.

In the next Chapter we shall see how to use the desktop applications from the GUI interface.

CHAPTER 4 • DESKTOP GUI INTERFACE - DESKTOP APPLICATIONS

4.1 Overview
In this Chapter we shall see how to access and use the desktop applications of our Raspberry pi 3.

4.2 Desktop GUI Applications
If you have connected a monitor, a mouse, and a keyboard to your raspberry Pi 3 computer then you can access the desktop GUI interface by entering command **startx** in the command mode.

If you wish to access the Desktop GUI applications from a desktop or a laptop computer then the required steps are as follows:

- **Step 1:** Connect to your Raspberry Pi using the Putty terminal emulator with the SSH services as explained in earlier chapters.

- **Step 2:** Run the VNC server by entering the following command into your SSH window:

    pi@raspberrypi ~ $ **vncserver :1**

- **Step 3**: Run the **VNC Viewer** program on your computer. Enter the IP address of your Raspberry Pi 3 computer, followed by characters :1 to indicate that we are using port 1 (see Figure 4.1). Click the **Connect** button.

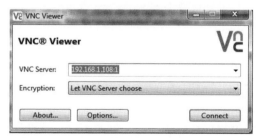

Figure 4.1 Enter the IP address of your Pi

You will see the window as in Figure 4.2. Just click **Continue**.

Figure 4.2 Click Continue

You will be asked for your password that you created earlier. Enter the password as shown in Figure 4.3.

Figure 4.3 Enter the password

You should see the Raspberry Pi 3 Desktop GUI environment as in Figure 4.4. On the top left corner of the screen, starting from the left hand side we have the following menus:

- Applications menu
- Web Browser
- File Manager
- Terminal
- Mathematica
- Wolfram

On the top right hand side of the screen, starting from the left we have the following menus:

- Bluetooth
- Wi-Fi
- Volume Control
- Time

Figure 4.4 Raspberry Pi 3 Desktop GUI

4.2.1 Applications Menu

Figure 4.5 shows the items under the Applications Menu.

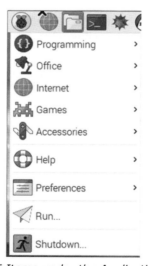

Figure 4.5 Items under the Applications Menu

Programming: This menu item includes a number of programming languages that we can use to program our Raspberry Pi 3. Figure 4.6 shows a list of the items in the Programming menu.

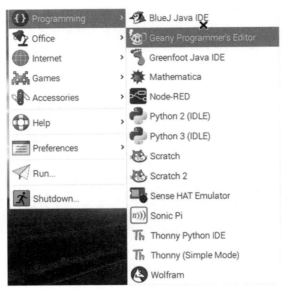

Figure 4.6 Items under the Programming menu

For example, clicking Python 2 (IDLE) starts the Python interpreter (see Figure 4.7) where we can create new Python files, edit existing files, save and print files, or run a Python program.

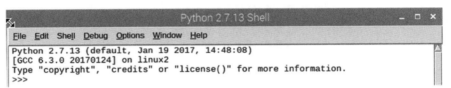

Figure 4.7 Starting the Python interpreter

Office: Figure 4.8 shows the applications under the Office menu. Here, we have office applications to create documents (LibreOffice Writer), to user draw applications (LibreOffice Draw), calculator (LibreOffice Calc), mathematics (LibreOffice Math), and power point application (LibreOffice Impress). The details and use of the office applications are beyond the scope of this book. Interested readers can find detailed information on the Internet, or the application Help menus can be used to get help on using an application.

Figure 4.8 Items under the Office menu

Internet: Figure 4.9 shows the items under the Internet menu. The Chromium Web Browser, Mail, Raspberry Pi resources, the Magpie, and the VNC Viewer are inside this menu.

Figure 4.9 Items under the Internet menu

Games: As shown in Figure 4.10, The games menu has two items: Minecraft, and Python Games. Python Games menu contains a large number of games as shown in Figure 4.11.

Figure 4.10 Items under the Games menu

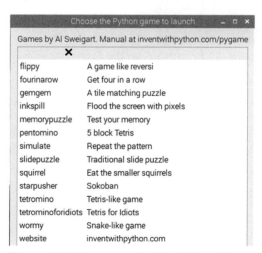

Figure 4.11 Games under the Python Games

Accessories: This menu, as shown in Figure 4.12, contains various applications such as archiver, calculator, file manager, image viewer, pdf viewer, and so on.

Figure 4.12 Items under the Accessories menu

Help: The help menu provides help on the use of the Raspberry Pi.

Preferences: As shown in Figure 4.13, this menu includes applications such as adding/removing software, Bluetooth manager, audio device settings, mouse and keyboard settings and so on.

Figure 4.13 Items under the Preferences menu

Shutdown: This menu item is used to shut down the Raspberry Pi computer orderly. As shown in Figure 4.14, the menu options are: Shutdown, reboot, and logout.

Figure 4.14 Shutdown menu options

4.2.2 Web Browser Menu

The Web Browser menu is next to the Applications menu and is used for web browsing.

4.2.3 File Manager Menu

This menu item is used for file handling and is similar to the File Explorer on Windows systems.

4.2.4 Terminal Menu

This menu item enables the command mode so that you can enter commands in this mode.

4.2.5 Mathematica

This menu item is the Mathematica which is a computational programming tool mainly used in engineering calculations.

4.2.6 Wolfram

Wolfram is a general purpose programming language developed by the Wolfram Research and is mainly used in mathematical applications.

4.2.7 Manage Bluetooth Devices

This is the first menu item at the top right hand side of the screen. This menu item is used to manage Bluetooth devices, such as turning Bluetooth on and off, pairing Bluetooth devices, adding Bluetooth devices and so on. Figure 4.15 shows the items under this menu.

Figure 4.15 Items under the Bluetooth menu

4.2.8 Wi-Fi

The next menu item to the Bluetooth is the Wi-Fi menu which can be used to tirn the Wi-Fi on and off, and to connect to a Wi-Fi router. When clicked, a list of the available Wi-Fi devices is given (see Figure 4.16).

Figure 4.16 Wi-Fi menu

4.2.9 Audio Volume Control

This menu item is used to control the audio volume (see Figure 4.17) through a sliding bar.

Figure 4.17 Audio volume control

Next to the volume control the CPU loading (as a percentage) and the date and time are shown (see Figure 4.18).

Figure 4.18 Showing the date

4.3 Summary

In this Chapter we had briefly looked at the Desktop GUI applications. Perhaps the most useful application for us is the Python programming interface.

In the next Chapter we shall be looking at how to use the Linux text editors **nano** and **vi** which can be very useful during program development.

CHAPTER 5 • USING A TEXT EDITOR IN LINUX COMMAND MODE

A text editor is used to create or modify the contents of a text file. There are many text editors available for the Linux operating system. Some popular ones are: nano, vim, vi, and many more. In this chapter we shall be looking at some of these text editors and see how to use them.

5.1 nano Text Editor

Start the **nano** text editor by entering the word nano, followed by the filename you wish to create or modify. An example is given below where a new file called **first.txt** is created:

pi@raspberrypi ~ $ **nano first.txt**

You should see the editor screen as in Figure 5.1. The name of the file to be edited is written at the top middle part of the screen. The message "New File" at the bottom of the screen shows that this is a newly created file. The shortcuts at the bottom of the screen are there to perform various editing functions. These shortcuts are accessed by pressing the Ctrl key together with another key. Some of the useful shortcuts are given below:

Ctrl+W: Search for a word

Ctrl+V: Move to next page

Ctrl+Y: Move to previous page

Ctrl+K: Cut the current row of txt

Ctrl+R: Read file

Ctrl+U: Paste the text you previously cut

Ctrl+J: Justify

Ctrl+\: Search and replace text

Ctrl+C: Display current column and row position

Ctrl+G: Get detailed help on using the nano

Ctrl+-: Go to specified line and column position

Ctrl+O: Save (write out) the file currently open

Ctrl+X: Exit nano

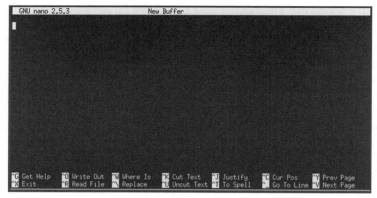

Figure 5.1 nano text editor screen

Now, type the following text as shown in Figure 5.2:

> nano is a simple and yet powerful text editor.
> This simple text example demonstrates how to use nano.
> This is the last line of the example.

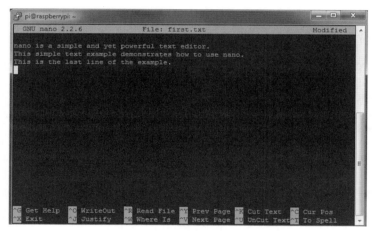

Figure 5.2 Sample text

The use of **nano** is now demonstrated with the following steps:

- **Step 1:** Go the beginning of the file by moving the cursor.

- **Step 2:** Look for word **simple** by pressing **Ctrl+W** and then typing **simple** in the window opened at the bottom left hand corner of the screen. Press the Enter key. The cursor will be positioned on the word **simple** (see Figure 5.3).

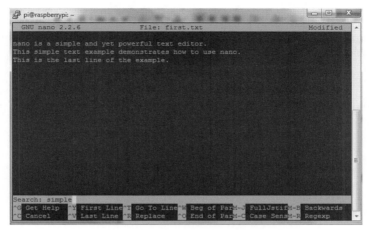

Figure 5.3 searching word **simple**

- **Step 3:** Cut the first line by placing the cursor anywhere on the line and then pressing Ctrl+K. The first line will disappear as in Figure 5.4.

Figure 5.4 Cutting the first line

- **Step 4:** Paste the line cut after the first line. Place the cursor on the second line and press **Ctrl+U** (see Figure 5.5).

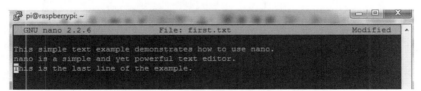

Figure 5.5 Paste the line cut previously

- **Step 5:** Place cursor at the beginning of word simple on the first row. Enter **Ctrl+C**. The row and column positions of this word will be displayed at the bottom of the screen (Figure 5.6).

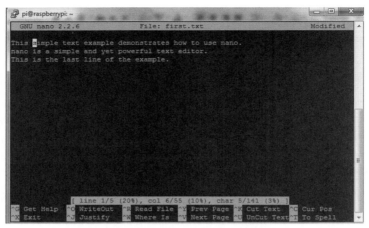

Figure 5.6 Displaying row and column position of a word

- **Step 6:** Press **Ctrl+G** to display help page as in Figure 5.7. Notice that the display is many pages long and you can jump to the next pages by pressing **Ctrl+Y** or to the previous pages by pressing **Ctrl+V**. Press **Ctrl+X** to exit the help page.

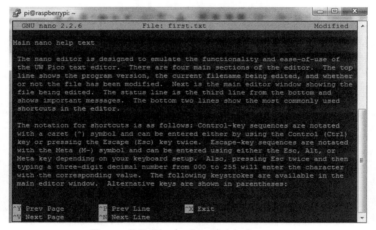

Figure 5.7 Displaying the help page

- **Step 7:** Press **Ctrl+-** and enter line and column numbers as 2 and 5, followed by the Enter key, to move cursor to line 2, column 5 (see Figure 5.8).

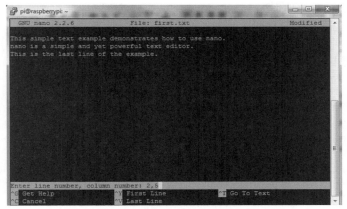

Figure 5.8 Moving to line 2, column 5

- **Step 8:** Replace word **example** with word **file**. Press **Ctrl+** and type the first word as **example** (see Figure 5.9). Press Enter and then type the replacement word as **file**. Press Enter and accept the change by typing y.

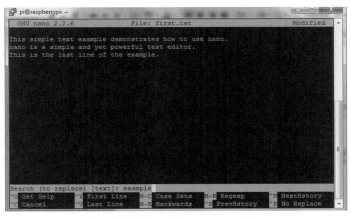

Figure 5.9 Replacing text

- **Step 9:** Save the changes. Press **Ctrl+X** to exit the file. Type **Y** to accept the saving, then enter the filename to be written to, or simply press Enter to write to the existing file (**first.txt** in this example). The file will be saved in your current working directory.

- **Step 10:** Display the contents of the file:

      pi@raspberrypi ~ $ **cat firs.txt**
      This simple text file demonstrates how to use nano.
      Nano is a simple and yet powerful text editor
      This is the last line of the example.
      pi@raspberrypi ~ $

In summary, **nano** is a simple and yet powerful text editor allowing us to create new text files or to edit existing files.

5.2 vi Text Editor

The **vi** text editor has been around for many years where it has been the standard Unix operating system default text editor. The **vi** editor is a fully featured powerful text editor for doing many different tasks. The only problem with using **vi** is that it is not very user friendly and learning may take some time. In this section we shall be looking at the basic features of this editor and see how we can use it in simple editing applications.

Notice that you cannot use the keyboard arrow keys with the **vi** editor. Some of the useful **vi** editor commands are listed below:

ZZ	save changes and exit vi
:wq	save changes and exit vi
:q!	exit without saving changes
h	move cursor left (backwards)
j	move cursor down
k	move cursor up
l	move cursor right (spacebar)
$	move to the last column on current line
o	move cursor to the first column on current line
w	move cursor to the beginning of the next word
b	move cursor to the beginning of the previous word
H	move cursor to the top of the screen
M	move cursor to the middle of the screen
L	move cursor to the bottom of the screen
G	move to the last line in the file
nG	move to line n
r	replace character under cursor with next character typed
i	insert before cursor
a	append after cursor
A	append at end of line
x	delete character under cursor
dd	delete line under cursor
dw	delete word under cursor
/	search for a word (forwards)
?	search a word (backwards)
:s	search and replace a word in current line

Start the **vi** text editor by typing **vi** followed by the name of the file to be created or modified. In this example it is assumed that anew file called **myfile.txt** is to be created:

pi@raspberrypi ~ $ **vi myfile.txt**

You should see the **vi** text editor screen displayed as in Figure 5.10. The name of the file being edited is displayed at the bottom of the screen.

*Figure 5.10 **vi** text editor screen*

The **vi** editor is different from most other text editors in that it is not possible to start typing inside the editor window. The steps for editing this file are given below:

- **Step 1:** The **vi** editor have different modes and you must be in the insert mode to be able to write to the window. Press *i* to move to the insert mode. Then type in the following text (see Figure 5.11):

    The vi text editor is a very powerful text editor.
    But it is not easy to use this editor.
    This exercise should help you understand the basic commands.

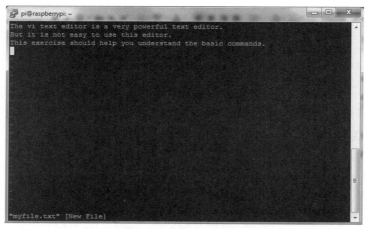

Figure 5.11 Entering the text

- **Step 2:** To come out of the insert mode, press the ESC key. To save the file, type characters **:w**. You can exit the editor after saving the changes by typing **:q**. Alternatively, you can type **ZZ** (note upper case) to save and exit. If you made changes to the file and attempt to quit without saving, you will get an error message. If you want to exit without saving the changes, simply type **:q!**

- **Step 3:** Make sure you are in the command mode and type the character **/** followed by a word to search for this word in the text. For example, type **/editor** to search for the word **editor** (see Figure 5.12) in the text.

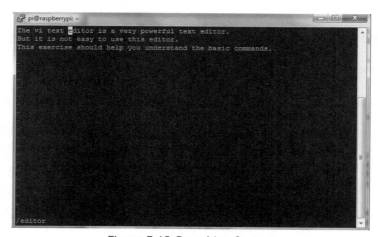

Figure 5.12 Searching for text

- **Step 4:** Insert word **is** before word **editor**. Type **i** followed by **is** and space, and terminate insert mode by pressing ESC key.

- **Step 5:** Move cursor right by pressing the **l** key. Similarly, move cursor left by pressing the **h** key. Move cursor down (to the second line) by pressing the **j** key.

- **Step 6:** Search for word **this** and delete it. Type **/this** followed by the Enter key. Type **dw** to delete the word.

- **Step 7:** Delete the second line where the cursor is on by typing **dd**

- **Step 8:** Search for word **help** and replace it with word **guide**. Go to the line where word help is. Type **/help**, then type **:s/help/guide/**

- **Step 9:** We can search and replace a word in any other line than the current line. For this example, position the cursor on the first line. Change word **basic** in the second line to **BASIC**. Type:

    :1,2s/basic/BASIC/

Notice that we can specify the range of lines by separating them with a comma. In this example, the search starts from line 1 and terminates at line 2.

5.3 Summary
Text editors are useful in creating new text files, or for modifying the contents of a text file. Notice that a text editor is not same as a word processing software. Word processing software inserts additional control characters inside a text such as bold, underline, and other formatting characters.

In this chapter we have seen how to use two of the popular Linux text editors: **nano** and **vi**.

CHAPTER 6 • RASPBERRY PI 3 HARDWARE INTERFACING

6.1 Overview

This chapter is about the Raspberry Pi 3 hardware interface and hardware development boards. In this chapter, we explore the various ways of connecting the Raspberry Pi 3 board to external electronic circuits.

The Raspberry Pi 3 is connected to external electronic circuits and devices using its GPIO (General Purpose Input Output) port connector. This is a 2.54mm, 40-pin expansion header, arranged in a 2x20 strip as shown in Appendix A and is also repeated here in Figure 6.1.

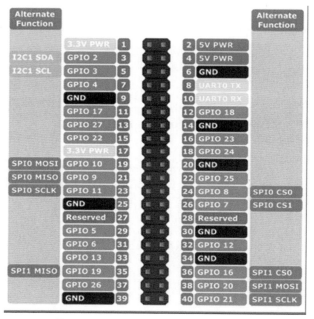

Figure 6.1 Raspberry Pi 3 GPIO pins

6.2 Raspberry Pi 3 GPIO Pin Definitions

When the GPIO connector is at the far side of the board, the pins at the bottom, starting from the left of the connector are numbered as 1, 3, 5, 7, and so on, while the ones at the top are numbered as 2, 4, 6, 8 and so on.

The GPIO provides 26 general purpose bi-directional I/O pins. Some of the pins have multiple functions. For example, pins 3 and 5 are the GPIO2 and GPIO3 input-output pins respectively. These pins can also be used as the I2C bus I2C SDA and I2C SCL pins respectively. Similarly, pins 9,10,11,19 can either be used as general purpose input-output, or as the SPI bus pins. Pins 8 and 10 are reserved for UART serial communication.

Two power outputs are provided: +3.3V and +5.0V. The GPIO pins operate at +3.3V logic levels (not like many other computer circuits that operate with +5V). A pin can either be an input or an output. When configured as an output, the pin voltage is either 0V (logic 0) or +3.3V (logic 1). Raspberry Pi 3 is normally operated using an external power supply (e.g. a mains adapter) with +5V output and minimum 2A current capacity. A 3.3V output pin can supply up to 16mA of current. The total current drawn from all output pins should not exceed the 51mA limit. Care should be taken when connecting external devices to the GPIO pins as drawing excessive currents or short-circuiting a pin can easily damage your Pi. The amount of current that can be supplied by the 5V pin depends on many factors such as the current required by the Pi itself, current taken by the USB peripherals, camera current, HDMI port current, and so on.

When configured as an input, a voltage above +1.7V will be taken as logic 1, and a voltage below +1.7V will be taken as logic 0. Care should be taken not to supply voltages greater than +3.3V to any I/O pin as large voltages can easily damage your Pi. The Raspberry Pi 3, like others in the family has no over-voltage protection circuitry.

6.3 Raspberry Pi 3 Hardware Development Boards and Hardware Tools
There are several hardware development boards and hardware tools that help the user to interface to the Raspberry Pi 3 safely and easily. Some of the tools require that you solder components to a board, while with some others you simply make wire connections without soldering by using a breadboard.

Some of the commonly used development boards and tools are described briefly in this section. It is strongly recommended by the author that you should use one of these tools and not make direct connections to the GPIO pins.

6.3.1 Raspberry Pi Compute Module 3 Lite
This is a small form factor SODIMM module Raspberry Pi 3 processor (see Figure 6.2) for embedded applications where the user can integrate it in their designs. The board contains the ARM Cortex-A53 processor with an edge connector.

Figure 6.2 Raspberry Pi Compute 3 Lite

6.3.2 Perma-Proto HAT
This is a plug-in daughter board (Figure 6.3) from Adafruit (https://thepihut.com) with

0.1 inch prototyping soldering holes for attaching components. It is useful during project development.

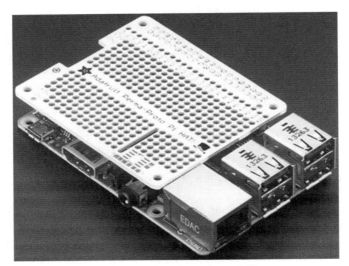

Figure 6.3 Perma-proto HAT

6.3.3 Explorer HAT

This is a small breadboard (Figure 6.4) from Adafruit that can be very useful during the development of projects with the Raspberry Pi. The board features 5V tolerant inputs, powered 5V outputs, capacitive touch pads, coloured LEDs, and crocodile clip pads.

Figure 6.4 Explorer HAT

6.3.4 Four Letter pHAT

This is a 4 character LED type display (Figure 6.5) that is compatible with the Raspberry Pi. There are four 14-segment displays that can be programmed to display text and numbers.

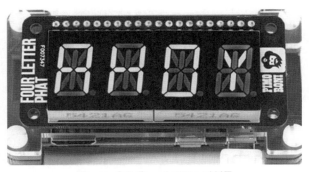

Figure 6.5 Four Letter pHAT

6.3.5 Mini RTC Module for Raspberry Pi

This Raspberry Pi compatible board is a real time clock (RTC) module (Figure 6.6) for the Raspberry Pi computers.

Figure 6.6 Mini RTC Module for raspberry Pi

6.3.6 Sense HAT

This is a Raspberry Pi compatible sensor board (Figure 6.7) having the following sensors on board:

- Pressure
- Temperature
- Humidity
- Accelerometer
- Gyroscope
- Magnetometer

In addition, an 8 x 8 LED matrix and a small 5 button joystick are provided.

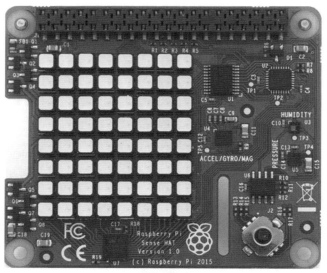

Figure 6.7 Sense HAT

6.3.7 Scroll pHAT

This Raspberry Pi compatible board (Figure 6.8) provides 11 x 5 matrix white LEDs with brightness control that can be programmed to display scrolling messages.

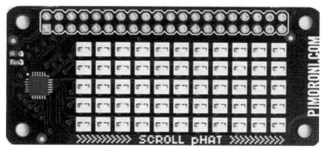

Figure 6.8 Scroll pHAT

6.3.8 Touch pHAT

This is a small Raspberry Pi compatible board with 6 touch sensitive buttons and LEDs. The board can be used in touch sensitive control applications.

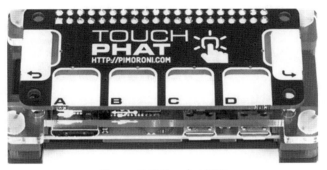

Figure 6.9 Touch pHAT

6.3.9 Motor Control Kit

The Pololu DRV8835 is a small Raspberry Pi compatible board (Figure 6.10) from Pololu (https://www.pololu.com) that can be plugged onto the GPIO pins to provide motor driving capability to a Raspberry Pi. The board can drive a pair of brushed DC motors.

Figure 6.10 Motor control kit

6.3.10 DC and Stepper Motor Driver HAT

This Raspberry Pi compatible module can drive both DC and stepper motors (Figure 6.11), available from www.robotshop.com. The current capacity is 1.2A per channel, with 3A peak current capability.

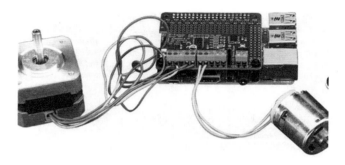

Figure 6.11 DC and stepper motor driver HAT

6.3.11 Raspberry Pi GPS Module

This module (Figure 6.12) is attached to one of the USB ports of Raspberry Pi 3 and provides GPS capability to the Pi (www.robotshop.com).

Figure 6.12 Raspberry Pi GPS Module

6.3.12 Raspberry Pi Camera Module

The camera module (Figure 6.13) provides 8 mega-pixel resolution and it can be used to take high-resolution video or still pictures (www.elektor.com).

Figure 6.13 Raspberry Pi camera module

6.3.13 Touch Display
This is a 7 inch TFT touch display compatible with the Raspberry Pi. The display has a res-olution of 1024x800 pixels (www.elektor.com).

Figure 6.14 Touch display

6.3.14 MotoPi – Servo Motor Control Board
This expansion board (Figure 6.15) can control up to 5 servo motors (www.elektor.com).

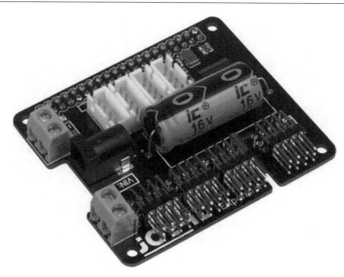

Figure 6.15 MotoPi motor control board

6.4 Summary

In this chapter we have looked at the pin configuration of the GPIO connector and the specifications of various Raspberry Pi 3 compatible hardware development boards and tools. It is recommended to use such tools for safe interfacing of electronic circuits and devices to your Pi.

In the next Chapter we shall be developing projects for our Raspberry Pi 3.

CHAPTER 7 • RASPBERRY PI 3 SIMPLE PROJECTS

7.1 Overview

In this chapter we shall be developing various Raspberry Pi 3 based projects. We shall start with very simple projects to make the reader familiar with the way that Raspberry Pi 3 projects can be developed using the Python programming language. More complex projects will be developed in later sections of this Chapter.

The following will be given for each project:

- Project title
- Description
- Aim
- Raspberry Pi type
- Block diagram
- Circuit diagram
- Construction
- PDL (optional, if necessary)
- Program listing
- Program description
- Suggestions (optional, if necessary)

7.2 PROJECT 1 – FLASHING AN LED

Description: This is perhaps the easiest hardware project you can design using your Raspberry Pi 3. In this project we will connect an LED to one of the ports of the Raspberry Pi 3 and then flash the LED at a rate of once a second.

Aim: The aim of this project is to show how a simple Python program can be written and then run from a file. The project also shows how to connect an LED to a Raspberry Pi 3 GPIO pin. In addition, the project shows how to use the GPIO library to configure and set a GPIO pin to logic 0 or 1.

Raspberry Pi Type: This project will run on all types of Raspberry Pi.

Block diagram: The block diagram of the project is shown in Figure 7.1

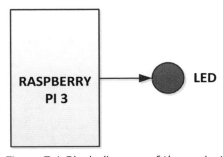

Figure 7.1 Block diagram of the project

Circuit diagram: The circuit diagram of the project is shown in Figure 7.2. A small LED is connected to port pin GPIO 2 (pin 3) of the Raspberry Pi 3 through a current limiting resistor. The value of the current limiting resistor is calculated as follows:

The output high voltage of a GPIO pin is 3.3V. The voltage across an LED is approximately 1.8V. The current through the LED depends upon the type of LED used and the amount of required brightness. Assuming that we are using a small LED, we can assume a forward LED current of about 3mA. Then, the value of the current limiting resistor is:

R = (3.3V – 1.8V) / 3mA = 500 ohm. We can choose a 470 ohm resistor

In Figure 7.2 the LED is operated in current sourcing mode where a high output from the GPIO pin drives the LED. The LED can also be operated in current sinking mode where the other end of the LED is connected to +3.3V supply and not to the ground. In current sinking mode the LED is turned ON when the GPIO pin is at logic low.

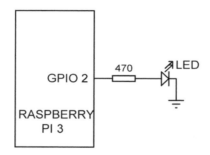

Figure 7.2 Circuit diagram of the project

Construction: The project is constructed on a breadboard as shown in Figure 7.3. Female-male jumper cables are used to connect the LED to the GPIO port. Notice that the short side of the LED must be connected to ground.

Figure 7.3 Constructing the project on a breadboard

Project PDL: The project PDL is shown in Figure 7.4.

```
BEGIN
     Import GPIO library
     Import time library
     Configure GPIO 2 as output
     DO FOREVER
         Turn ON LED
         Wait 1 second
         Turn OFF LED
         Wait 1 second
     ENDDO
END
```

Figure 7.4 Project PDL

Program listing: The program is called **LED.py** and the listing is shown in Figure 7.5. The program was written using the **nano** text editor. At the beginning of the program the **RPi.GPIO** and the **time** modules are imported to the project. Then the pin numbering is configured to use the BCM notation. GPIO 2 is configured as an output pin. The rest of the program is executed indefinitely in a **while** loop where the LED is turned on and off with one second delay between each output. Enter Cntrl+C to terminate the program.

```
#----------------------------------------------------------
#
#                    FLASHING LED
#                    ============
#
# In this project a small LED is connected to GPIO 2 of
# the Raspberry Pi 3. The program flashes the LED every
# second.
#
# Program: LED.py
# Date    : October 2017
# Author : Dogan Ibrahim
#----------------------------------------------------------
import RPi.GPIO as GPIO    # import GPIO library
import time                # import time library
GPIO.setwarnings(False)    # disable warning messages

GPIO.setmode(GPIO.BCM)     # set BCM pin numbering
GPIO.setup(2, GPIO.OUT)    # configure GPIO 2 as output

while True:
    GPIO.output(2, 1)         # turn ON LED
    time.sleep(1)             # wait 1 second
    GPIO.output(2, 0)         # turn OFF LED
    time.sleep(1)             # wait 1 second
```

Figure 7.5 Program listing of the project

The program is run from the command mode as follows:

pi@raspberrypi ~ $ **python LED.py**

If you wish to run the program from the GUI Desktop environment, you should use the VNC Viewer to get into the GUI desktop screen. Then, click the **Applications menu -> Programming -> Python (IDLE 2)**. You should see the screen as in Figure 7.6.

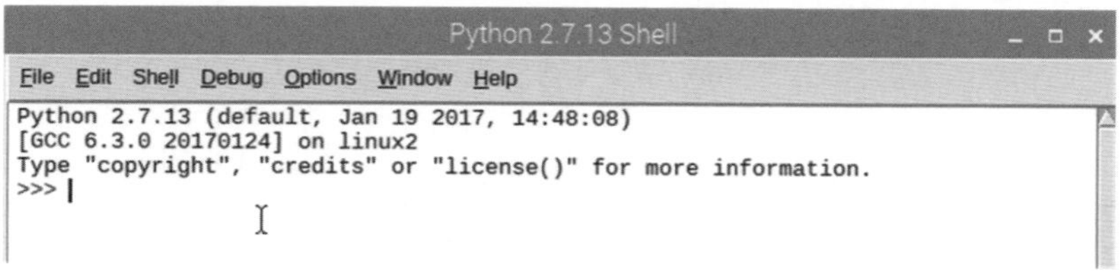

Figure 7.6 Activate Python in GUI Desktop

Click **File** and open file **LED.py**. You should see the program displayed as in Figure 7.7.

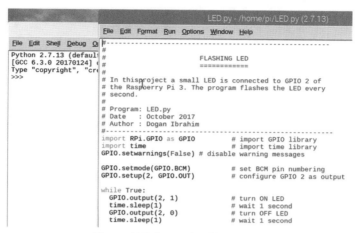

Figure 7.7 Open the file LED.py

Now, click **Run -> Run Module** to run the program. You should see the LED flashing every second. To terminate the program, close the screen by clicking the **X** character at the top right corner of the screen and click **OK** to kill the program (Figure 7.8).

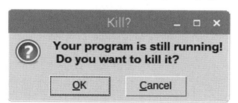

Figure 7.8 Terminating the program

You can copy the program from your Raspberry Pi 3 home directory to your PC using the **winSCP** file copy program (available free of charge on the Internet).

Recommended modifications: The program given in Figure 7.5 can be made more user friendly by assigning meaningful names to various variables in the program. The modified program (LED2.py) is shown in Figure 7.9.

```
#----------------------------------------------------------
#
#                    FLASHING LED
#                    ============
#
# In thisproject a small LED is connected to GPIO 2 of
# the Raspberry Pi 3. The program flashes the LED every
# second.
#
```

```
# This version of the program is more user friendly
#
# Program: LED2.py
# Date    : October 2017
# Author  : Dogan Ibrahim
#-----------------------------------------------------------
import RPi.GPIO as GPIO    # import GPIO library
import time                # import time library
GPIO.setwarnings(False)    # disable warning messages


LED = 2        # LED on GPIO 2
ON = 1
OFF = 0


GPIO.setmode(GPIO.BCM)     # set BCM pin numbering
GPIO.setup(LED, GPIO.OUT)  # configure LED as output


while True:
    GPIO.output(2, ON)     # turn ON LED
    time.sleep(1)          # wait 1 second
    GPIO.output(2, OFF)    # turn OFF LED
    time.sleep(1)          # wait 1 second
```

Figure 7.9 Modified program

Note: You may find it easier to create and run your Python programs from the GUI desktop interface (IDLE 2) since the correct indentation is automatically placed in your code as you type the code.

7.3 PROJECT 2 – BINARY COUNTING WITH 8 LEDs

Description: In this project 8 LEDs are connected to the Raspberry Pi 3 GPIO pins. The LEDs count up in binary every second. .

Aim: The aim of this project is to show how 8 LEDs can be connected to the Raspberry Pi 3 GPIO pins. In addition, the project shows how to group the LEDs as an 8-bit port and control them as a single port.

Raspberry Pi Type: This project will run on all types of Raspberry Pi.

Block diagram: The block diagram of the project is shown in Figure 7.10

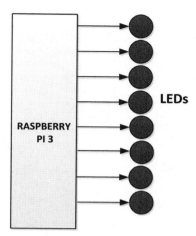

Figure 7.10 Block diagram of the project

Circuit diagram: The circuit diagram of the project is shown in Figure 7.11.The LEDs are connected to 8 GPIO pins through 470 Ohm current limiting resistors. The following 8 GPIO pins are grouped as an 8-bit port, where GPIO 2 is configured as the LSB and GPIO 9 is configured as the MSB:

```
          MSB                           LSB
GPIO:     9   10  22  27  17  4    3    2
Pin no:   21  19  15  13  11  7    5    3
```

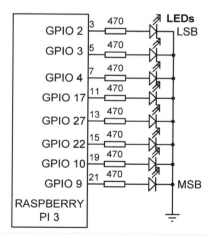

Figure 7.11 Circuit diagram of the project

Construction: The project is constructed on a breadboard as shown in Figure 7.12. Female-male jumper cables are used to connect the LEDs to the GPIO port. Notice that the short side of the LED must be connected to ground.

Figure 7.12 Constructing the project on a breadboard

Project PDL: The project PDL is shown in Figure 7.13.

```
BEGIN
    Import GPIO library
    Import time library
    CALL Configure_Port to configure the port as output
    Set cnt = 0
    DO FOREVER
        CALL Port_Output with cnt
        Wait 1 second
        Increment cnt
    ENDDO
END

BEGIN/Configure_Port
    IF port is output THEN
        CALL GPIO.setup to configure the port as output
    ELSE
        CALL GPIO.setup to configure the port as input
    ENDIF
END/Configure_Port
```

```
BEGIN/Port_Ouput
  CALL GPIO.output to send the byte to the port
END/Port_Output
```

Figure 7.13 Project PDL

Program listing: The program is called **LEDCNT.py** and the listing is shown in Figure 7.14. The program was written using the **nano** text editor. At the beginning of the program the **RPi.GPIO** and the **time** modules are imported to the project. Then the pin numbering is configured to use the BCM notation. All the 8 GPIO channels used in the project are configured as outputs using function **Configure_Port**. Notice that the **Configure_Port** function is general and list **DIR** sets the directions of the GPIO pins. An "O" sets as an output and an "I" sets as an input. Then, a loop is formed to execute forever and inside this loop the LEDs count up by one in binary. Variable **cnt** is used as the counter. Function **Port_Output** is used to control the LEDs. This function can take integer numbers from 0 to 255 and it converts the input number (x) into binary using the built-in function **bin**. Then the leading "0b" characters are removed from the output string **b** (**bin** function inserts characters "0b" to the beginning of the converted string). Then, the converted string **b** is made up of 8 characters by inserting leading 0s. The string is then sent to the PORT bit by bit, starting from the most-significant bit (GPIO 9) position

```
#-------------------------------------------------------------
#
#                   BINARY UP COUNTING LEDs
#                   =======================
#
# In this project 8 LEDs are connected to the following
# GPIO pins:
#
# 9 10 22 27 17 4 3 2
#
# The program groups these LEDs as an 8-bit port and then
# the LEDs count up in binary with one second delay between
# each output.
#
# Program: LEDCNT.py
# Date    : October 2017
# Author : Dogan Ibrahim
#-------------------------------------------------------------
import RPi.GPIO as GPIO               # import GPIO library
import time                          # import time library
GPIO.setwarnings(False)              # disable warning messages
GPIO.setmode(GPIO.BCM)               # set BCM pin numbering
PORT = [9, 10, 22, 27, 17,  4,  3,  2] # port connections
DIR = ["0","0","0","0","0","0","0","0"] # port directons

#
```

```
# This function configures the port pins as outputs ("0") or
# as inputs ("I")
#
def Configure_Port():
    for i in range(0, 8):
        if DIR[i] == "0":
            GPIO.setup(PORT[i], GPIO.OUT)
        else:
            GPIO.setup(PORT[i], GPIO.IN)
    return


#
# This function sends 8-bit data (0 to 255) to the PORT
#
def Port_Output(x):
    b = bin(x)                      # convert into binary
    b = b.replace("0b", "")         # remove leading "0b"
    diff = 8 - len(b)               # find the length
    for i in range (0, diff):
        b = "0" + b                 # insert leading os

    for i in range (0, 8):
        if b[i] == "1":
            GPIO.output(PORT[i], 1)
        else:
            GPIO.output(PORT[i], 0)
    return


#
# Configure PORT to all outputs
#
Configure_Port()


#
# Main program loop. Count up in binary every second
#
cnt = 0
while True:
    Port_Output(cnt)        # send cnt to port
    time.sleep(1)           # wait 1 second
    cnt = cnt + 1           # increment cnt
```

Figure 7.14 Program listing

Recommended modifications: Modify the program such that the LEDs count down every two seconds.

7.4 PROJECT 3 – CHRISTMAS LIGHTS (RANDOM FLASHING 8 LEDs)

Description: In this project 8 LEDs are connected to the Raspberry Pi 3 GPIO pins. The LEDs flash randomly every 0.5 seconds just like fancy Christmas lights.

Aim: The aim of this project is to show how 8 LEDs can be connected to the Raspberry Pi 3 GPIO pins. In addition, the project shows how to generate random numbers between 1 and 255 and then shows how to use these numbers to turn the individual LEDs ON and OFF randomly.

Raspberry Pi Type: This project will run on all types of Raspberry Pi.

Block diagram: The block diagram of the project is as shown in Figure 7.10

Circuit diagram: The circuit diagram of the project is as shown in Figure 7.11.The LEDs are connected to 8 GPIO pins through 470 Ohm current limiting resistors.

Construction: The project is constructed on a breadboard as shown in Figure 7.12.

Project PDL: The project PDL is shown in Figure 7.15.

```
BEGIN
    Import GPIO library
    Import time library
    Import random number library
    CALL Configure_Port to configure the port as output
    DO FOREVER
        Get a random number between 1 and 255
        CALL Port_Output to send the number to the LEDs
        Wait 0.5 second
    ENDDO
END


BEGIN/Configure_Port
    IF port is output THEN
        CALL GPIO.setup to configure the port as output
    ELSE
        CALL GPIO.setup to configure the port as input
    ENDIF
END/Configure_Port



BEGIN/Port_Ouput
    CALL GPIO.output to send the byte to the port
END/Port_Output
```

Figure 7.15 Project PDL

Program listing: The program is called **XMAS.py** and the listing is shown in Figure 7.16. The program was written using the **nano** text editor. At the beginning of the program the **RPi.GPIO, time,** and **random** modules are imported to the project. Then the pin numbering is configured to use the BCM notation. All the 8 GPIO channels used in the project are configured as outputs using function **Configure_Port** as in the previous project. Then, a loop is formed to execute forever and inside this loop a random number is generated between 1 and 255, and this number is used as an argument to function **Port_Output.** The binary pattern corresponding to the generated number is sent to the port which turns the LEDs ON or OFF in a random manner.

```
#------------------------------------------------------------
#
#                    CHRISTMAS LIGHTS
#                    ================
#
# In this project 8 LEDs are connected to the Raspberry Pi 3
# and these LEDs flash randomly at 0.5 second intervals. The
# connections of the LEDs are to the following GPIO pins:
#
# 9 10 22 27 17 4 3 2
#
# The program groups these LEDs as an 8-bit port and then
# generates random numbers between 1 and 255 and turns the
# LEDs ON and OFF depending on the generated number.
#
# Program: XMAS.py
# Date    : October 2017
# Author : Dogan Ibrahim
#------------------------------------------------------------
import RPi.GPIO as GPIO              # import GPIO library
import time                         # import time library
import random                       # import random library
GPIO.setwarnings(False)             # disable warning messages
GPIO.setmode(GPIO.BCM)              # set BCM pin numbering
PORT = [9, 10, 22, 27, 17,  4,  3,  2] # port connections
DIR = ["0","0","0","0","0","0","0","0"] # port directons

#
# This function configures the port pins as outputs ("0") or
# as inputs ("I")
#
def Configure_Port():
    for i in range(0, 8):
        if DIR[i] == "0":
            GPIO.setup(PORT[i], GPIO.OUT)
        else:
```

```
        GPIO.setup(PORT[i], GPIO.IN)
    return


#
# This function sends 8-bit data (0 to 255) to the PORT
#
def Port_Output(x):
    b = bin(x)                  # convert into binary
    b = b.replace("0b", "")     # remove leading "0b"
    diff = 8 - len(b)           # find the length
    for i in range (0, diff):
        b = "0" + b             # insert leading os

    for i in range (0, 8):
        if b[i] == "1":
            GPIO.output(PORT[i], 1)
        else:
            GPIO.output(PORT[i], 0)
    return
#
# Configure PORT to all outputs
#
Configure_Port()


#
# Main program loop. Count up in binary every second
#
while True:
    numbr = random.randint(1, 255)  # generate a random number
    Port_Output(numbr)              # send cnt to port
    time.sleep(0.5)                 # wait 0.5 second
```

Figure 7.16 Program listing

Recommended modifications: Modify the program such that 10 LEDs can be connected to the Raspberry Pi 3 and flashed randomly.

7.5 PROJECT 4 – ROTATING LEDs WITH PUSH-BUTTON SWITCH
Description: In this project 8 LEDs are connected to the Raspberry Pi 3 GPIO pins as in the previous project. In addition, a push-button switch is connected to one of the GPIO ports. The LEDs rotate in one direction when the button is not pressed, and in the opposite direction when the button is pressed. Only one LED is ON at any time. One second delay is inserted between each output.

Aim: The aim of this project is to show a push-button switch can be connected to a GPIO pin.

Raspberry Pi Type: This project will run on all types of Raspberry Pi.

Block diagram: The block diagram of the project is shown in Figure 7.17.

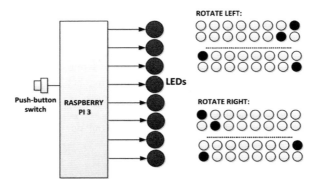

Figure 7.17 Block diagram of the project

Circuit diagram: The circuit diagram of the project is shown in Figure 7.18.The LEDs are connected to 8 GPIO pins through 470 Ohm current limiting resistors as in the previous project. The push-button switch is connected to GPIO 11 (pin 23) of the Raspberry Pi 3. The push-button switch is connected through a 10K and a 1K resistor. When the switch is not pressed the input is at logic 1. When the switch is pressed the input changes to logic 0. Notice that the 1K resistor is used here for safety if the input channel is configured as an output by mistake. If this is the case, without a resistor the output would be short-circuited and this could damage the Raspberry Pi hardware.

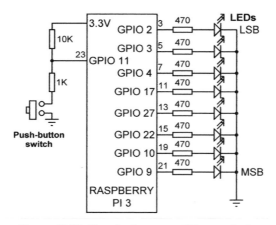

Figure 7.18 Circuit diagram of the project

Construction: The project is constructed on a breadboard as shown in Figure 7.19.

Figure 7.19 Project constructed on a breadboard

Project PDL: The project PDL is shown in Figure 7.20.

```
BEGIN
    Import GPIO library
    Import time library
    CALL Configure_Port to configure the port as output
    Configure GPIO 11 as input
    Set rot = 1
    DO FOREVER
        IF button is pressed THEN
            Shift rot left
        ELSE
            Shift rot right
        ENDIF
        CALL Port_Output to send rot to the LEDs
        Wait one second
    ENDDO
END

BEGIN/Configure_Port
    IF port is output THEN
        CALL GPIO.setup to configure the port as output
    ELSE
        CALL GPIO.setup to configure the port as input
    ENDIF
END/Configure_Port
```

```
BEGIN/Port_Ouput
    CALL GPIO.output to send the byte to the port
END/Port_Output
```

Figure 7.20 Project PDL

Program listing: The program is called **rotate.py** and the listing is shown in Figure 7.21. The program was written using the **nano** text editor. At the beginning of the program the **RPi.GPIO**, and **time** modules are imported to the project. Then the pin numbering is configured to use the BCM notation. All the 8 GPIO channels used in the project are configured as outputs using function **Configure_Port** as in the previous project. Then, a loop is formed to execute forever and inside this loop variable **rot** is used as an argument to the **Port_Output** function. If the button is not pressed then **rot** is shifted right and the LED ON sequence is from left to right (from MSB to LSB). If on the other hand the button is pressed then the LED On sequence is from right to left (from LSB to MSB). One second delay is inserted between each output.

```
#------------------------------------------------------------------
#
#                    ROTATING LEDs WITH PUSH-BUTTON
#                    ==============================
#
# In this project 8 LEDs are connected to the Raspberry Pi 3.
# In addition, a push-button switch is connected to GPIO 11
# (pin 23) through resistors. Normally the output of the button
# is at logic 1 and goes to logic 0 when the button is pressed.
# The LEds rotate in one direction when the button is not pressed
# and in the opposite direction when the button is pressed.
#
# Connections of the LEDs are to the following GPIO pins:
#
# 9 10 22 27 17 4 3 2
#
# On second delay is inserted between each output.
#
# Program: rotate.py
# Date    : October 2017
# Author : Dogan Ibrahim
#------------------------------------------------------------------
import RPi.GPIO as GPIO              # import GPIO library
import time                         # import time library
GPIO.setwarnings(False)             # disable warning messages
GPIO.setmode(GPIO.BCM)              # set BCM pin numbering
PORT = [9, 10, 22, 27, 17,  4,  3,  2]    # port connections
```

```
DIR =  ["0","0","0","0","0","0","0","0"] # port directions
GPIO.setup(11, GPIO.IN)                  # GPIO 11 is input


#
# This function configures the port pins as outputs ("0") or
# as inputs ("I")
#
def Configure_Port():
    for i in range(0, 8):
        if DIR[i] == "0":
            GPIO.setup(PORT[i], GPIO.OUT)
        else:
            GPIO.setup(PORT[i], GPIO.IN)
    return


#
# This function sends 8-bit data (0 to 255) to the PORT
#
def Port_Output(x):
    b = bin(x)                   # convert into binary
    b = b.replace("0b", "")      # remove leading "0b"
    diff = 8 - len(b)            # find the length
    for i in range (0, diff):
        b = "0" + b              # insert leading os

    for i in range (0, 8):
        if b[i] == "1":
            GPIO.output(PORT[i], 1)
        else:
            GPIO.output(PORT[i], 0)
    return
#
# Configure PORT
#
Configure_Port()

#
# Main program loop. Rotate the LEDs
#
rot = 1
while True:
  Port_Output(rot)
  time.sleep(1)                # wait 1 second
  if GPIO.input(11) == 0:      # button pressed?
    rot = rot << 1             # shift left
    if rot > 128:              # at the end
```

```
    rot = 1              # back to beginning
  else:                  # button not pressed
    rot = rot >> 1       # shift right
    if rot == 0:         # at the end
      rot = 128          # back to beginning
```

Figure 7.21 Program listing

7.6 PROJECT 5 – MORSE CODE EXERCISER WITH BUZZER

Description: In this project a buzzer is connected to GPIO 2 of the Raspberry Pi 3. The user enters a text from the keyboard. The buzzer is then turned ON and OFF to sound the letters in Morse code.

Aim: The aim of this project is to show how a buzzer can be connected to a Raspberry Pi 3, and also how to use various statements in Python programs.

Raspberry Pi Type: This project will run on all types of Raspberry Pi.

Block diagram: The block diagram of the project is shown in Figure 7.22.

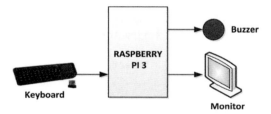

Figure 7.22 Block diagram of the project

Circuit diagram: The circuit diagram of the project is shown in Figure 7.23 where an active buzzer is connected to GPIO 2 of the Raspberry Pi 3.

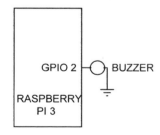

Figure 7.23 Circuit diagram of the project

Project PDL: In a Morse code each letter is made up of dots and dashes. Figure 7.24 shows the Morse code of all the letters in the English alphabet (this table can be extended by adding the Morse code of numbers and punctuation marks). The following rules apply to the timing of dots and dashes:

The duration of a dot is taken as the unit time and this determines the speed of the transmission. Normally the speed of transmission is quoted in words per minute (wpm). The standard required minimum in Morse code based communication is 12 wpm.

- The duration of a dash is 3 unit times
- The time between each dot and dash is a unit time
- The time between the letters is 3 unit times
- The time between the words is 7 unit times

The unit time in milliseconds is calculated using the following formula:

Time (ms) = 1200/wpm

In this project the Morse code is simulated at 10wpm. Thus, the unit time is taken to be 1200/10 = 120ms.

```
Letter       Morse code
   A :    . -
   B :    - . . .
   C :    - . - .
   D :    - . .
   E :    .
   F :    . . - .
   G :    - - .
   H :    . . . .
   I :    . .
   J :    . - - -
   K :    - . -
   L :    . - . .
   M :    - -
   N :    - .
   O :    - - -
   P :    . - - .
   Q :    - - . -
   R :    . - .
   S :    . . .
   T :    -
   U :    . . -
   V :    . . . -
   W :    . - -
   X :    - . . -
   Y :    - . - -
   Z :    - - . .
```

Figure 7.24 Morse code of English letters

The project PDL is shown in Figure 7.25.

```
BEGIN
    Import GPIO library
    Import time library
    Configure channel 2 as an output pin
    DO until text QUIT is received
        Read text from the keyboard
        IF space detected (inter-word character) THEN
            CALL Do_SPACE
        ELSE
            DO for all letters of the text
                Find the Morse code
                IF the code contains a dot THEN
                    CALL DO_DOT
                ELSE IF code contains a dash THEN
                    CALL DO_DASH
                ENDIF
            ENDDO
        Wait 2 seconds
    ENDDO
    Cleanup the I/O resources used
END


BEGIN/DO_DOT
    Send 1 to GPIO pin 2
    Wait 120ms (unit time)
    Send 0 to GPIO pin 2
    Wait 120ms (unit time)
END/DO_DOT


BEGIN/DO_DASH
    Send 1 to GPIO pin 2
    Wait 360ms (3 x unit time)
    Send 0 to GPIO pin 2
    Wait 120ms (unit time)
END/DO_DASH


BEGIN/DO_SPACE
    Wait 7 unit time
END/DO_SPACE
```

Figure 7.25 Project PDL

Program listing: The program is called **morse.py** and the listing is shown in Figure 7.26. At the beginning of the program the **RPi.GPIO** and the **time** modules are imported to the project. Then the pin numbering is configured to use the BCM notation. GPIO 2 is configured as an output pin and this is where the buzzer is connected to. The Morse code alphabet is stored in list **Morse_Code**. Function **DO_DOT** implement a single dot with a duration of one unit time. Function **DO_DASH** implement a single dash with duration of 3 unit times. Function **DO_SPACE** implements a space character with duration of 7 unit times. The rest of the program is executed in a loop where a text is read from the keyboard and the buzzer sounds in such a way to represent the Morse code of this text. The program terminates if the user enters the text **QUIT**.

You should run the program from the command mode as follows:

pi@raspberrypi:~ $ **python3 morse.py**

```
#-------------------------------------------------------------------
#
#                       MORSE CODE EXERCISER
#                       ====================
#
# This project can be used to learn the Morse code. A buzzer is
# connected to GPIO 2 of the Raspberry Pi 3.
#
# The program reads a text from the keyboard and then sounds the
# buzzer to simulate sending or receiving the Morse code of this
# text.
#
# In this project the Morse code speed is assumed to be 10 wpm,
# but can easily be changed by changing the parameter wpm.
#
# File   : morse.py
# Date   : October, 2017
# Author: Dogan Ibrahim
#-------------------------------------------------------------------
import RPi.GPIO as GPIO       # import GPIO module
import time                   # import time module
GPIO.setwarnings(False)

Pin = 2
words_per_minute = 10         # define words per min
wpm = 1200/words_per_minute   # unit time in milliseconds
unit_time = wpm / 1000

GPIO.setmode(GPIO.BCM)        # set BCM pin numbering
GPIO.setup(Pin, GPIO.OUT)     # Configure GPIO 2 as output
```

```python
Morse_Code = {
        'A': '.-',
        'B': '-...',
        'C': '-.-.',
        'D': '-..',
        'E': '.',
        'F': '..-.',
        'G': '--.',
        'H': '....',
        'I': '..',
        'J': '.---',
        'K': '-.-',
        'L': '.-..',
        'M': '--',
        'N': '-.',
        'O': '---',
        'P': '.--.',
        'Q': '--.-',
        'R': '.-.',
        'S': '...',
        'T': '-',
        'U': '..-',
        'V': '...-',
        'W': '.--',
        'X': '-..-',
        'Y': '-.--',
        'Z': '--..'
        }

#
# This function sends a DOT (unit time)
#
def DO_DOT():
    GPIO.output(Pin, 1)
    time.sleep(unit_time)
    GPIO.output(Pin, 0)
    time.sleep(unit_time)
    return

#
# This function sends a DASH ( 3*unit time)
#
def DO_DASH():
    GPIO.output(Pin, 1)
    time.sleep(3*unit_time)
    GPIO.output(Pin, 0)
```

```
        time.sleep(unit_time)
        return

#
# This function sends inter-word space (7*unit time)
#
def DO_SPACE():
    time.sleep(7*unit_time)
    return

#
# Main program code
#
text = ""
while text != "QUIT":
    text = input("Enter text to send: ")
    if text != "QUIT":
        for letter in text:
            if letter == ' ':
                DO_SPACE()
            else:
                for code in Morse_Code[letter.upper()]:
                    if code == '-':
                        DO_DASH()
                    elif code == '.':
                        DO_DOT()
                    time.sleep(unit_time)
        time.sleep(2)
```

Figure 7.26 Program listing of the project

Recommended Modifications: An LED can be connected to the GPIO pin instead of the buzzer so that the Morse code can be seen in visual form.

7.7 PROJECT 6 – ULTRASONIC MOSQUITO REPELLER

Description: In this project a Pulse Width Modulated (PWM) waveform with a frequency of 40 kHz and duty cycle of 50% is generated. This waveform is used to drive an ultrasonic transducer that is known to repel mosquitos.

Aim: The aim of this project is to show a PWM waveform with a specified frequency and duty cycle can be generated.

Raspberry Pi Type: This project will run on all types of Raspberry Pi.

Background: PWM waves are frequently used in power control applications. The waveform is basically a positive square wave with variable ON and OFF times. As shown in Figure 7.27, the total of the ON and OFF times is known as the period of the waveform. The ratio of the ON time to the period is known as the Duty Cycle and it is represented as a percentage. i.e.

Duty Cycle = (T / P) x 100%

where, T is the ON time, and P is the period (ON time + OFF time).

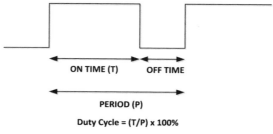

ON TIME (T)   OFF TIME

PERIOD (P)

Duty Cycle = (T/P) x 100%

Figure 7.27 PWM waveform

By varying the duty cycle from 0% to 100% we can easily control a load, e.g. a motor. For example, at 50% duty cycle the load receives half of the total power. Similarly, at 100% duty cycle the load receives full power.

Block diagram: The block diagram of the project is shown in Figure 7.28.

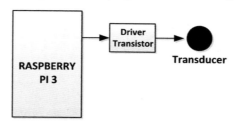

Figure 7.28 Block diagram of the project

Circuit diagram: The circuit diagram of the project is shown in Figure 7.29. The ultrasonic transducer is connected to GPIO 2 pin of the Raspberry Pi 3 through a transistor switch. The transducer is powered from an external voltage.

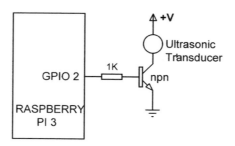

Figure 7.29 Circuit diagram of the project

Project PDL: The project PDL is shown in Figure 7.30.

```
BEGIN
  Import GPIO library
  Configure GPIO 2 as output
  Generate PWM waveform with frequency 40 kHz and Duty Cycle 50%
END
```

Figure 7.30 Project PDL

Program listing: The program is called **pwm.py** and the listing is shown in Figure 7.31. At the beginning of the program the **RPi.GPIO** module is imported to the project. Port GPIO 2 is configured as an output where the transducer is connected through a switching power transistor.

```
#---------------------------------------------------------------
#
#               ULTRASONIC MOSQUITO REPELLER
#               ============================
#
# In this program an ultrasonic transducer is connected to
# GPIO 2 of the Raspberry Pi 3 through a switching power
# transistor. The program generates a PWM waveform with a
# frequency of 40 kHz and the duty cycle of 50%.
#
# File  : pwm.py
# Date  : October, 2017
# Author: Dogan Ibrahim
#---------------------------------------------------------------
import RPi.GPIO as GPIO     # import GPIO module
GPIO.setwarnings(False)

GPIO.setmode(GPIO.BCM)
GPIO.setup(2, GPIO.OUT)     # Configure GPIO 2 output

p = GPIO.PWM(2, 40000)      # generate PWM waveform
p.start(50)                 # set duty cycle to 50%

while True:                 # wait here
    pass
```

Figure 7.31

GPIO pin 2 is configured as a PWM port with a frequency of 40 kHz using the following statement:

P = GPIO.PWM(2, 40000)

Then, the PWM is started with 50% Duty Cycle using the statement:

```
p.start(50)
```

```
#---------------------------------------------------------------
#
#                    ULTRASONIC MOSQUITO REPELLER
#                    ============================
#
# In this program an ultrasonic transducer is connected to
# GPIO 2 of the Raspberry Pi 3 through a switching power
# transistor. The program generates a PWM waveform with a
# frequency of 40 kHz and the duty cycle of 50%.
#
# File  : pwm.py
# Date  : October, 2017
# Author: Dogan Ibrahim
#---------------------------------------------------------------
import RPi.GPIO as GPIO      # import GPIO module
GPIO.setwarnings(False)

GPIO.setmode(GPIO.BCM)
GPIO.setup(2, GPIO.OUT)      # Configure GPIO 2 output

p = GPIO.PWM(2, 40000)       # generate PWM waveform
p.start(50)                  # set duty cycle to 50%

while True:                  # wait here
    pass
```

Figure 7.32 Program listing

The PWM library supports the following commands:

P = GPIO.PWM(channel, frequency)   - Configure channel for PWM with
                                        specified frequency

p.start(DC)   - Start PWM with specified Duty Cycle

p.stop()   - Stop PWM

p.ChangeFrequency(frequency)   - Change PWM frequency

p.ChangeDutyCycle(DC)   - Change Duty Cycle

7.8 PROJECT 7 – ELECTRONIC DICE

Description: In this project 7 LEDs are arranged in the form of the faces of a dice and a push-button switch is used. When the button is pressed, the LEDs turn ON to display numbers 1 to 6 as if on a real dice. The display is turned OFF after 3 seconds, ready for the next game.

Aim: The aim of this project is to show how a dice can be constructed with 7 LEDs.

Raspberry Pi Type: This project will run on all types of Raspberry Pi.

Block diagram: The block diagram of the project is shown in Figure 7.33.

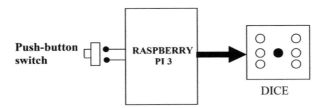

Figure 7.33 Block diagram of the project

Figure 7.34 shows the LEDs that should be turned ON to display the 6 dice numbers.

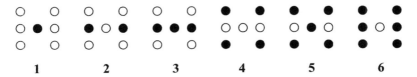

Figure 7.34 LED Dice

Circuit diagram: The circuit diagram of the project is shown in Figure 7.35. Here, 8 GPIO pins are collected together to form a PORT. The following pins are used for the LEDs (there are 7 LEDs, but 8 port pins are used in the form of a byte where the most-significant bit position is not used):

PORT bit	7	6	5	4	3	2	1	0
GPIO:		9	10	22	27	17	4	3	2

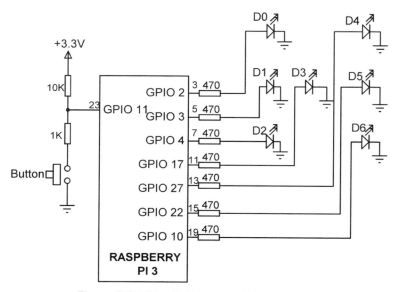

Figure 7.35 Circuit diagram of the project

The push-button switch is connected to port pin GPIO 11.

Construction: The project is constructed on a breadboard as shown in Figure 7.36. The LEDs are mounted to represent the dots on a real dice.

Figure 7.36 Project construction on a breadboard

Project PDL: The project PDL is shown in Figure 7.37.

```
BEGIN
     Import GPIO library
     Import time library
     Import random library
     Configure GPIO 11 as input
     Create DICE_NO list for LED bit patterns
     CALL Configure_Port to configure the PORT as output
     Declare callback handler (DICE) on pin GPIO 11
          DO FOREVER
               Wait for the button to be pressed
          ENDDO
END


BEGIN/Configure_Port
     IF port is output THEN
          CALL GPIO.setup to configure the port as output
     ELSE
          CALL GPIO.setup to configure the port as input
     ENDIF
END/Configure_Port



BEGIN/Port_Ouput
     CALL GPIO.output to send the byte to the port
END/Port_Output


BEGIN/DICE
     Generate a random number between 1 and 6
     Get the LED bit pattern corresponding to this number
     CALL Port_Output to send the data to the LEDs
     Wait 3 seconds
     Turn OFF all LEDs
END/DICE
```

Figure 7.37 Project PDL

Table 7.1 gives the relationship between a dice number and the corresponding LEDs to be turned ON to imitate the faces of a real dice. For example, to display number 1 (i.e. only the middle LED is ON), we have to turn LED D3 ON. Similarly, to display number 4, we have to turn ON D0, D2, D4 and D6.

Required number	LEDs to be turned on
1	D3
2	D1, D5
3	D1, D3, D5
4	D0, D2, D4, D6
5	D0, D2, D3, D4, D6
6	D0, D1, D2, D4, D5, D6

Table 7.1 Dice number and LEDs to be turned ON

The relationship between the required number and the data to be sent to the PORT to turn on the correct LEDs is given in Table 7.2. For example, to display dice number 2, we have to send hexadecimal 0x22 to the PORT. Similarly, to display number 5, we have to send hexadecimal 0x5D to the PORT and so on.

Required number	PORT data (Hex)
1	0x08
2	0x22
3	0x2A
4	0x55
5	0x5D
6	0x77

Table 7.2 Required number and PORT data

Program listing: The program is called **dice.py** and the listing is shown in Figure 7.38. At the beginning of the program the **RPi.GPIO, time**, and **random** modules are imported to the project. Then, port pins are declared as a list in variable PORT, and the direction of each pin is declared as output ("O") in a list variable called DIR. The bit pattern to be sent to the LEDs corresponding to each dice number is stored in hexadecimal format in a list called DICE_NO (see Table 7.2).

The pin numbering is configured to use the BCM notation. GPIO 11 is configured as an input pin and the push-button switch is connected to this pin to simulate the "throwing" of a dice. A callback routine called DICE is created so that when the button is pressed the program jumps to this function. The callback function is setup to trigger when the button is pressed (i.e. when it goes from logic 1 to 0). Switch debouncing is also used in the callback routine. Inside the callback function a random number is generated between 1 and 6. Then list DICE_NO is used to find the LEDs that should be turned ON, and the required bit pattern is sent to the PORT to display the dice number. The program displays the dice number for 3 seconds and then all the LEDs are turned OFF to indicate that the program is ready for the next game.

```
#------------------------------------------------------------
#
#                      ELECTRONIC DICE
#                      ===============
#
# This program is an electronic dice. GPIO 11 of Raspberry Pi 3
# is configured as an input and a push-button switch is connected
# to this port pin. When the button is pressed a random dice number
# is displayed between 1 and 6 on the LEDs.
#
# 7 LEDs are mounted on the breadboard in the form of the face of
# a real dice. The following GPIO pins are used for the LEDs (bit
# 7 is mot used):
#
#   Port pin: 7  6  5  4  3 2 1 0
#   GPIO    :    10 22 27 17 4 3 2
#
# The following PORT pins are used to construct the dice:
#
# D0      D4
# D1 D3 D5
# D2      D6
#
# Program: dice.py
# Date    : October, 2017
# Author : Dogan Ibrahim
#------------------------------------------------------------
import RPi.GPIO as GPIO       # import GPIO library
import time                   # import time library
import random                 # import random library
GPIO.setwarnings(False)


PORT = [9, 10, 22, 27, 17, 4, 3, 2]

DICE_NO = [0, 0x08, 0x22, 0x2A, 0x55, 0x5D, 0x77]


#
# This function configures the port directions
#
def Configure_Port():
    for i in range (0, 8):
            GPIO.setup(PORT[i], GPIO.OUT)
    return


#
# This function sends a byte (8-bit) data to the PORT
```

```
#
def Port_Output(x):
    b = bin(x)            # convert into binary
    b = b.replace("0b", "")     # remove leading 0b
    diff = 8 - len(b)     # find the difference
    for i in range (0, diff):
        b = "0" + b        # insert leading 0s

    for i in range (0, 8):
        if b[i] == "1":
            GPIO.output(PORT[i], 1)
        else:
            GPIO.output(PORT[i], 0)
    return


#
# The program jumps here after the button is pressed
#
def DICE(dummy):
    n = random.randint(1, 6)    # generate a random number
    pattern = DICE_NO[n]        # find the pattern
    Port_Output(pattern)        # turn ON required LEDs
    time.sleep(3)               # wait for 3 seconds
    Port_Output(0)              # turn OFF all LEDs
    return


#
# Start of main program
#
Dice_Pin = 11
GPIO.setmode(GPIO.BCM)

GPIO.setup(Dice_Pin, GPIO.IN)
#
# Configure PORT as outputs
#
Configure_Port()
#
# Setup callback to function DICE when the button is pressed
#
GPIO.add_event_detect(Dice_Pin, GPIO.FALLING, bouncetime=50,
                      callback=DICE)
#
# Program waits here for the button to be pressed, then a random
# number is generated between 1 and 6 and is displayed on the LEDs
#
```

```
while True:
    pass          # Do nothing
```

Figure 7.38 Program listing of the project

7.9 PROJECT 8 – USING AN I2C LCD – SECONDS COUNTER

Description: In this project an I2C type LCD is connected to the Raspberry Pi 3. The program counts up in seconds and displays on the LCD.

Aim: The aim of this project is to show how an I2C type LCD can be used in Raspberry Pi projects.

Raspberry Pi Type: This project will run on all types of Raspberry Pi (see the section on circuit diagram for supplying power to the LCD).

Block Diagram: Figure 7.39 shows the block diagram of the project.

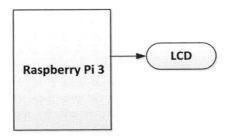

Figure 7.39 Block diagram of the project

Circuit Diagram: The circuit diagram of the project is shown in Figure 7.40. The I2C LCD has 4 pins: GND, +V, SDA, and SCL. SDA is connected to pin GPIO 2 and SCL is connected to pin GPIO 3. +V pin of the display should be connected to the +5V (pin 2) of the Raspberry Pi 3 (some versions of Raspberry Pi, such as the Raspberry Pi Zero and Raspberry Pi Zero W cannot supply enough power to drive the LCD. It is recommended to use an external +5V supply to power for the LCD if you are using one of these models). Note that there is no problem mixing the +3.3V GPIO pins of the Raspberry Pi with the +5V of the I2C LCD. This is because the Raspberry Pi is the I2C master device and the SDA and SCL lines are pulled up to +3.3V through resistors. SCL line is the clock which is always output from the master device. The slave device (I2C LCD here) only pulls down the SDA line when it acknowledges the receipt of data and it does not send any data to the master device. Therefore, there are no voltage level problems as long as the Raspberry Pi I2C output pins can drive the I2C LCD inputs, which is the case here.

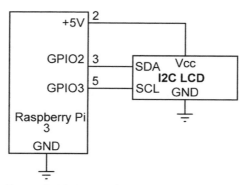

Figure 7.40 Circuit diagram of the project

The LCD used in this project is based on the I2C (or I²C) interface. I2C is a multi-slave, multi-master, single-ended serial bus used to attach low-speed peripheral devices to micro-controllers. The bus consists of only two wires called SDA and SCL where SDA is the data line and SCL is the clock line and up to 1008 slave devices can be supported on the bus. Both lines must be pulled up to the supply voltage by suitable resistors. The clock signal is always generated by the bus master. The devices on the I2C bus can communicate at 100 kHz or 400 kHz.

Figure 7.41 shows the front and back of the I2C based LCD. Notice that the LCD has a small board mounted at its back to control the I2C interface. The LCD contrast is adjusted through the small potentiometer mounted on this board. A jumper is provided on this board to disable the backlight if required.

Figure 7.41 I2C based LCD (front and back views)

Program Listing: Before using the I2C pins of the Raspberry Pi we have to enable the I2C peripheral interface on the device. The steps for this are as follows:

- Start the configuration menu from the command prompt:

    pi@raspberrypi:~ $ **sudo raspi-config**

- Go down the menu to **Interface Options**

- Go down and select **I2C**

- Enable the I2C interface

- Select **Finish** to complete

Now we have to install the I2C library on our Raspberry Pi 3. The steps are as follows:

- Enter the following commands from the command menu:

    pi@raspberrypi:~ $ **sudo apt-get update**
    pi@raspberrypi:~ $ **sudo apt-get install –y python-smbus i2c-tools**
    pi@raspberrypi:~ $ **sudo reboot**

- Enter the following command to test the installation. You should see **i2c_bcm2837** listed:

    pi@raspberrypi:~ $ **lsmod | grep i2c_**

- Modify the config file as follows:

    pi@raspberrypi:~ $ **sudo nano /etc/modules**

- Add the following lines (if they are not already there):

    i2c-bcm2837
    i2c-dev

- Exit from nano by typing Ctrl X and Y to save the file. You can check the Contents of this file by entering the command:

    pi@raspberrypi:~ $ **cat /etc/modules**

- Reboot the Raspberry Pi 3 by entering:

    pi@raspberrypi:~ $ **sudo reboot**

- Connect your LCD to the Raspberry Pi 3 device and enter the following command to check whether or not the LCD is recognized by the Raspberry Pi 3:

    pi@raspberrypi:~ $ **sudo i2cdetect –y 1**

You should see a table similar to the one shown below. A number in the table means that the LCD has been recognizes correctly and the I2C slave address of the LCD is shown in the table. In this example the LCD address is 27:

	1	2	3	4	5	6	7	8	9	a	b	c	d	e	f
00:				--	--	--	--	--	--	--	--	--	--	--	--
10:	--	--	--	--	--	--	--	--	--	--	--	--	--	--	--
20:	--	--	--	--	--	--	--	27	--		--	--	--	--	--

```
30:    --   --   --   --   --   --   --   --   --     --   --   --   --   --   --
40:    --   --   --   --   --   --   --   --   --     --   --   --   --   --   --
50:    --   --   --   --   --   --   --   --   --     --   --   --   --   --   --
60:    --   --   --   --   --   --   --   --   --     --   --   --   --   --   --
70:    --   --   --   --   --   --   --   --   --     --   --   --   --   --   --
```

We should now install an I2C LCD library so that we can send commands and data to our LCD. There are many Python libraries available for the I2C type LCDs. The one chosen here is called the **RPi_I2C_driver**. This library is installed as follows:

- Go to the following web link:

  https://gist.github.com/DenisFromHR/cc863375a6e19dce359d

- Scroll down to section **RPi_I2C_driver.py**. Click **Raw** at the top right hand side of the screen and save the file in a folder (e.g. Desktop) with the name **RPi_ I2C_driver.py** (the easiest option might be to copy the file into the Notebook and then save it as RPi_I2C_driver.py).

- Start your Raspberry Pi 3 in command mode.

- Start the WinSCP file copy utility (you should install it if you already do not have it) on your PC and copy file **RPi_I2C_driver.py** to folder **usr/lib/python2.7** on your Raspberry Pi 3.

- Check to make sure that the file is copied successfully. You should see the file listed with the command:

  pi@raspberrypi: ~ $ **ls /usr/lib/python2.7**

We are now ready to write our program. Figure 7.42 shows the program listing (**lcd.py**). At the beginning of the program libraries RPi.GPIO, timer, and the LCD driver library RPi_ I2C_driver are imported to the program. The heading SECONDS COUNTER is displayed for 2 seconds. The program then clears the LCD screen and enters into an infinite loop. Inside this loop variable **cnt** is incremented every second and the total value of **cnt** is displayed on the LCD continuously.

```
#----------------------------------------------------------------
#
#              I2C LCD SECONDS COUNTER
#              ========================
#
# In this program an I2C LCD is connected to the Raspberry Pi.
# The program counts up in seconds and displays on the LCD.
#
# At the beginning of the program the text SECONDS COUNTER is
```

```
# displayed for 2 seconds
#
# Program: lcd.py
# Date    : October 2017
# Author  : Dogan Ibrahim
#-----------------------------------------------------------
import time
import RPi_I2C_driver

LCD = RPi_I2C_driver.lcd()
LCD.lcd_clear()                             # clear LCD
LCD.lcd_display_string("SECONDS COUNTER", 1) # display string
time.sleep(2)                               # wait 2 seconds

cnt = 0                                     # initialize cnt
LCD.lcd_clear()                             # clear lcd
while True:                                 # infinite loop
    cnt = cnt + 1                           # increment count
    LCD.lcd_display_string_pos(str(cnt),1,1) # display cnt
    time.sleep(1)                           # wait one second
```

Figure 7.42 Program listing

The I2C LCD library supports the following functions (see the I2C LCD library documentation for more details):

lcd_clear()   clear LCD and set to home position
lcd_display_string(text, row)   display text at LCD row
lcd_write_char(c)   display character
lcd_write(cmd)   write command cmd to LCD
lcd.backlight(1/0)   enable/disable LCD backlight
lcd_display_string_pos(text,row,col)   display text at given row,column

7.10 PROJECT 9 – ANALOG TEMPERATURE SENSOR THERMOMETER

Description: In this project an analog temperature sensor chip is used to measure and then display the ambient temperature every second on the monitor. Because the Raspberry Pi does not have any analog-to-digital converters (ADC) on-board, an external ADC chip is used in this project.

Aim: The aim of this project is to show how an external ADC chip can be connected to a Raspberry Pi and how the temperature can be read and displayed on the monitor using an analog temperature sensor chip.

Raspberry Pi Type: This project will run on all types of Raspberry Pi.

Block Diagram: Figure 7.43 shows the block diagram of the project.

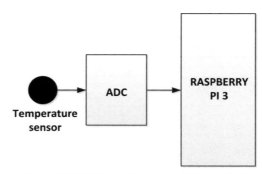

Figure 7.43 Block diagram of the project

Circuit Diagram: The dual MCP3002 ADC chip is used in this project to provide analog input capability to the Raspberry Pi. This chip has the following features:

- 10-bit resolution (0 to 1023 quantization levels)
- On-chip sample and hold
- SPI bus compatible
- Wide operating voltage (+2.7V to +5.5V)
- 75 Ksps sampling rate
- 5nA standby current, 50µA active current

The MCP3002 is a successive approximation 10-bit ADC with on-chip sample and hold amplifier. The device is programmable to operate as either differential input pair or as dual single-ended inputs. The device is offered in 8-pin package. Figure 7.44 shows the pin configuration of the MCP3002.

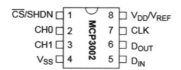

Figure 7.44 Pin configuration of the MCP3002

The pin definitions are as follows:

Vdd/Vref:	Power supply and reference voltage input
CH0:	Channel 0 analog input
CH1:	Channel 1 analog input
CLK:	SPI clock input
DIN:	SPI serial data in
DOUT:	SPI serial data out
CS/SHDN:	Chip select/shutdown input

In this project the supply voltage and the reference voltage are set to +3.3V. Thus, the digital output code is given by:

Digital output code = 1024 x Vin / 3.3

or,

Digital output code = 310.30 x Vin

each quantization level corresponds to 3300mV/1024 = 3.22mV. Thus, for example, input data "00 0000001" corresponds to 3.22mV, "00 0000010" corresponds to 6.44mV and so on.

The MCP3002 ADC has two configuration bits: SGL/DIFF and ODD/SIGN. These bits follow the sign bit and are used to select the input channel configuration. The SGL/DIFF is used to select single ended or pseudo-differential mode. The ODD/SIGN bit selects which channel is used in single ended mode and is used to determine polarity in pseudo-differential mode. In this project we are using channel 0 (CH0) in single ended mode. According to the MCP3002 data sheet, SGL/DIFF and ODD/SIGN must be set to 1 and 0 respectively.

Figure 7.45 shows the circuit diagram of the project. A TMP36DZ type analog temperature sensor chip is connected to CH0 of the ADC. TMP36DZ is a 3 terminal small sensor chip with pins: Vs, GND, and Vo. Vs is connected to +3.3V, GND is connected to system ground, and Vo is the analog output voltage. The temperature in degrees Centigrade is given by:

Temperature = (Vo – 500) / 10

Where, Vo is the sensor output voltage in millivolts.

CS, Dout, CLK, and Din pins of the ADC are connected to the SPI pins CE0, MISO, SCLK, and MOSI pins of the Raspberry Pi 3 respectively. Figure 7.46 shows the project constructed on a breadboard.

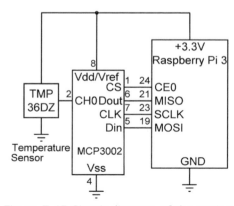

Figure 7.45 Circuit diagram of the project

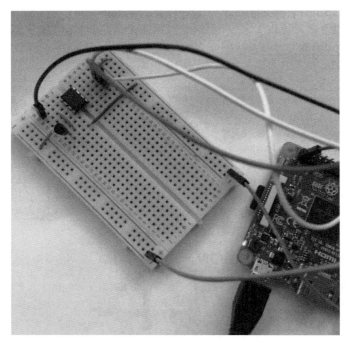

Figure 7.46 Project built on a breadboard

Program listing: Figure 7.47 shows the Raspberry Pi Python program listing (program: **tmp36.py**). Function **get_adc_data** is used to read the analog data, where the channel number (channel_no) is specified in the function argument as 0 or 1. Notice that we have to send the start bit, followed by the SGL/DIFF and ODD/SIGN bits and the MSBF bit to the chip.

It is recommended to send leading zeroes on the input line before the start bit. This is often done when using microcontroller based systems that must send 8 bits at a time.

The following data can be sent to the ADC (SGL/DIFF = 1 and ODD/SIGN = channel_no) as bytes with leading zeroes for more stable clock cycle. The general data format is:

0000 000S DCM0 0000 0000 0000

Where, S = start bit, D = SGL/DIFF bit, C = ODD/SIGN bit, M = MSBF bit
For channel 0: 0000 0001 1000 0000 0000 0000 (0x01, 0x80, 0x00)
For channel 1: 0000 0001 1100 0000 0000 0000 (0x01, 0xC0, 0x00)

Notice that the second byte can be sent by adding 2 to the channel number (to make it 2 or 3) and then shifting 6 bits to the left as shown above to give 0x80 or 0xC0.

The chip returns 24 bit data (3 bytes) and we must extract the correct 10 bit ADC data from this 24 bit data. The 24 bit data is in the following format ("X" is don't care bit):

XXXX XXXX XXXX DDDD DDDD DDXX

Assuming that the returned data is stored in 24 bit variable ADC, we have:

ADC[0] = "XXXX XXXX"
ADC[1] = "XXXX DDDD"
ADC[2] = "DDDD DDXX"

Thus, we can extract the 10 bit ADC data with the following operations:

(ADC[2] >> 2)   so, low byte = "00DD DDDD"

and

(ADC[1] & 15) << 6)   so, high byte = "DD DD00 0000"

Adding the low byte and the high byte we get the 10 bit converted ADC data as:

DD DDDD DDDD

The SPI bus on the Raspberry Pi supports the following functions:

Function	Description
open (0,0)	Open SPI bus 0 using CE0
open (0,1)	Open SPI bus 0 using CE1
close()	disconnect the device from the SPI bus
writebytes([array of bytes])	Write an array of bytes to SPI bus device
readbytes(len)	Read **len** bytes from SPI bus device
xfer2([array of bytes])	Send an array of bytes to the device with CEx asserted at all times
xfer([array of bytes])	Send an array of bytes de-asserting and asserting CEx with every byte transmitted

The module **spidev** must be imported at the beginning of the program before any of the above functions are called. Also, you must enable the SPI interface on your Raspberry Pi 3 in the configuration menu. The steps are:

• Get into command mode (e.g. from Putty)

• Enter the following command:

pi@raspberrypi:~ $ **sudo raspi-config**

- Select the Interface Options

- Enable SPI interface

- Finish and exit the configuration menu

At the beginning of the program in Figure 7.47 modules RPi.GPIO and spidev are imported to the program and an instance of the SPI is created. Function **get_adc_data** reads the temperature from sensor chip MCP3002 and returns a digital value between 0 and 1023. This value is then converted into millivolts, 500 is subtracted from it, and the result is divided by 10 to find the temperature in degrees Centigrade. The temperature is displayed on the monitor every second.

```
#-------------------------------------------------------------------
#
#                    ANALOG TEMPERATURE SENSOR
#                    =========================
#
# In this project a TMP36 type analog temperature chip is used
# to measure the ambient temperature. The temperature is read
# using a MCP3002 type ADC chip. The result is converted into
# degrees Centigrade and is displayed on the monitor
#
# Program: tmp36.py
# Date    : October 2017
# Author  : Dogan Ibrahim
#-------------------------------------------------------------------
import RPi.GPIO as GPIO
import spidev
import time
GPIO.setwarnings(False)
#
# Create SPI instance and open the SPI bus
#
spi = spidev.SpiDev()
spi.open(0,0)                         # we are using CE0 for CS

GPIO.setmode(GPIO.BCM)


#
# This function returns the ADC data read from the MCP3002
#
def get_adc_data(channel_no):
    ADC = spi.xfer2([1, (2 + channel_no) << 6, 0])
```

```
    rcv = ((ADC[1] & 15) << 6) + (ADC[2] >> 2)
    return rcv


#
# Start of main program. Read the analog temperature, convert
# into degrees Centigrade and display on the monitor every second
#
while True:
    adc = get_adc_data(0)
    mV = adc * 3300.0 / 1023.0          # convert to mV
    Temp = (mV - 500.0) / 10.0          # temperature in C
    print("Temperature = %f " %Temp)    # display temperature
    time.sleep(1)                       # wait one second
```

Figure 7.47 Python program listing

A typical display on the monitor is shown in Figure 7.48.

```
pi@raspberrypi:~ $ python tmp36.py
Temperature = 18.387097
Temperature = 18.387097
Temperature = 18.709677
Temperature = 18.387097
Temperature = 19.677419
Temperature = 21.612903
Temperature = 22.903226
Temperature = 24.193548
Temperature = 24.838710
```

Figure 7.48 Typical display

7.11 PROJECT 10 – REACTION TIMER

Description: This is a reaction timer project. The user presses a button as soon as he/she sees a LED lighting. The time delay between seeing the light and pressing the button is measured and displayed on the monitor. The LED then turns OFF and the process is repeated after a random delay of 1 to 10 seconds.

Aim: The aim of this project is to show how the time can be read and how a simple reaction timer project can be designed.

Raspberry Pi Type: This project will run on all types of Raspberry Pi.

Block Diagram: Figure 7.49 shows the block diagram of the project.

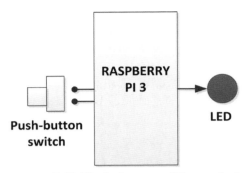

Figure 7.49 Block diagram of the project

Circuit Diagram: The circuit diagram of the project is very simple and it consists of an LED and a push-button switch. The LED and the button are connected to GPIO 2 and GPIO 3 respectively. The button is connected using two resistors as shown in Figure 7.50. Figure 7.51 shows the circuit built on a breadboard.

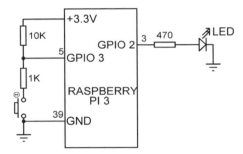

Figure 7.50 Circuit diagram of the project

Figure 7.51 Circuit built on a breadboard

Program listing: The program is called **reaction.py** and its listing is given in Figure 7.52. At the beginning of the program RPi.GPIO, time, and random libraries are imported. The button is configured as an input and the LED as an output. The program runs in a loop where the system time is recorded as soon as the LED is turned ON. The program waits for the user to press the button, and the system time is read again at this moment. The difference between this time and the first time is displayed as the reaction time of the user. This process repeats after a random delay of 1 to 10 seconds. Notice that the floating point function **time.time()** returns the time in seconds since the epoch.

```
#-----------------------------------------------------------
#
#                   REACTION TIMER
#
#                   ==============
#
# This is a reaction timer program. The user presses a button
# as soon as he/she see a light. The time between seeing the
# light and pressing the button is measured and is displayed
# in milliseconds as the reaction time of the user. The light
# comes ON after a random number of seconds between 1 and 10
# seconds.
#
```

```
# Program: reaction.py
# Date    : October 2017
# Author  : Dogan Ibrahim
#------------------------------------------------------------
import RPi.GPIO as GPIO
import time
import random

LED = 2
Button = 3

GPIO.setwarnings(False)
GPIO.setmode(GPIO.BCM)

#
# LED is output, button is input
#
GPIO.setup(Button, GPIO.IN)
GPIO.setup(LED, GPIO.OUT)

GPIO.output(LED, 0)
#
# Start of main program
#
while True:
    T = random.randint(1, 10)
    time.sleep(T)                           # random delay
    GPIO.output(LED, 1)                     # LED ON
    start_time = time.time()                # start time
    while (GPIO.input(Button) == 1):        # wait until button pressed
        pass
    end_time = time.time()                  # end time
    diff_time = 1000.0*(end_time - start_time)
    diff_int = int(diff_time)
    print("Reaction time=%d " %diff_int)    # display reaction time
    GPIO.output(LED, 0)                     # LED OFF
    time.sleep(3)                           # wait 3 seconds
```

Figure 7.52 Program listing

A typical display is shown in Figure 7.53.

```
pi@raspberrypi:~ $ python reaction.py
Reaction time=10454
Reaction time=353
Reaction time=14523
Reaction time=4233
```

Figure 7.53 Typical display

7.12 PROJECT 11 – AUTOMATIC DUSK LIGHTS

Description: In this project a light dependent resistor (LDR) is used to sense the darkness and a relay is activated when the ambient light intensity falls below the required level. It is possible to connect e.g. lights to the relay so that they turn ON automatically when for example it is dusk.

Aim: The aim of this project is to show how to use an LDR in a Raspberry Pi project, and also how to connect and activate a relay.

Raspberry Pi Type: This project will run on all types of Raspberry Pi.

Block Diagram: Figure 7.54 shows the block diagram of the project.

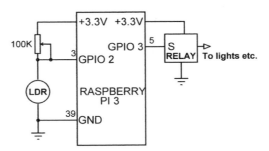

Figure 7.54 Block diagram of the project

Circuit Diagram: As shown in Figure 7.55, the circuit diagram of the project is very simple and it consists of an LDR, a 10K potentiometer, and a relay. The LDR is connected to GPIO 2, and the relay to GPIO 3. GPIO 2 and GPIO 3 are configured as input and output respectively.

The resistance of the LDR increases as the light level falls. The response of a typical LDR is shown in Figure 7.55. The LDR is connected as a resistive potential divider circuit. The voltage across the LDR increases as the light level falls. At a certain light level the voltage will be high enough to be accepted as logic 1 by the Raspberry Pi input. This point is detected and the relay is turned ON as soon as this happens. The potentiometer can be adjusted so that the relay is activated at the required light level. This process will require some trial and error.

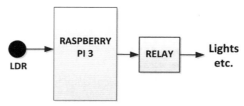

Figure 7.55 Circuit diagram of the project

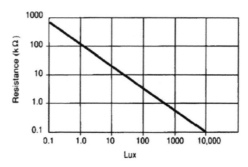

Figure 7.55 Response of a typical LDR

Program listing: Figure 7.56 shows the program listing (program: **dusklight.py**). The LDR and the relay are configured as inputs and outputs respectively. The program detects the voltage across the LDR and if it at logic 1 (i.e. dark) then it activates the relay, otherwise the relay is not activated. The potentiometer can be used to adjust the required light trigger level.

```
#-------------------------------------------------------------------
#
#                        DUSK LIGHT
#                        ==========
#
# In this project a light dependent resistor (LDR) is
# used to detect the ambient light level. When the light
# level falls below the required value, a relay is activated
# which turns ON the lights.
#
# The potentiometer can be used to adjust the triggering
# light level of the project.
#
# Program: dusklight.py
# Date    : October 2017
# Author : Dogan Ibrahim
#-------------------------------------------------------------------
import RPi.GPIO as GPIO
GPIO.setwarnings(False)
```

```
LDR = 2
RELAY = 3

GPIO.setmode(GPIO.BCM)
#
# Configure the LDR and RELAY ports
#
GPIO.setup(LDR, GPIO.IN)        # LDR is input
GPIO.setup(RELAY, GPIO.OUT)     # relay is output

GPIO.output(RELAY, 0)           # RELAY OFF to start with

while True:
    if GPIO.input(LDR) == 1:    # if dark
        GPIO.output(RELAY, 1)   # Activate RELAY
    else:
        GPIO.output(RELAY, 0)
```

Figure 7.56 Program listing

7.13 PROJECT 12 - PARKING SENSORS

Description: This is a parking sensors project to help a person park a car safely and easily. Pair of ultrasonic transmitter/receiver sensors are mounted in the front and back of a vehicle to sense the distance to the objects and a buzzer sounds if the sensors are too close to the objects in front of them. In this project safe distance is assumed to be 10cm.

Aim: The aim of this project is to show how ultrasonic sensors can be attached to a Raspberry Pi and how distance can be measured using these sensors.

Raspberry Pi Type: This project will run on all types of Raspberry Pi.

Block Diagram: Figure 7.57 shows the block diagram of the project.

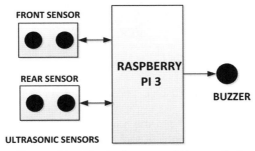

Figure 7.57 Block diagram of the project

Circuit Diagram: Pair of sensors are used to sense the distance both at the front and at the rear of a vehicle. The outputs of the ultrasonic sensors are +5V and therefore are not compatible with the inputs of Raspberry Pi. Resistive potential divider circuits are used to lower the voltage to +3.3V. The voltage at the output of the potential divider resistor is:

$$Vo = 5V \times 2K / (2K + 1K) = 3.3V$$

In this project, HC-SR04 type ultrasonic transmitter/receiver modules are used (see Figure 7.58). These modules have the following specifications:

- Operating voltage (current): 5V (2mA) operation
- Detection distance: 2cm – 450cm
- Input trigger signal: 10us TTL
- Sensor angle: not more than 15 degrees

The sensor modules have the following pins:

Vcc:	+V power
Trig:	Trigger input
Echo:	Echo output
Gnd:	Power ground

Figure 7.58 Ultrasonic transmitter/receiver module

The principle of operation of the ultrasonic sensor module is as follows:

- A 10us trigger pulse is sent to the module
- The module then sends eight 40kHz square wave signals and automatically detects the returned (echoed) pulse signal
- If an echo signal is returned the time to receive this signal is recorded
- The distance to the object is calculated as:

Distance to object (in metres) = (time to received echo in seconds * speed of sound) / 2

The speed of sound is 340 m/s, or 0.034 cm/µs

Therefore,

Distance to object (in cm) = (time to received echo in µs) * 0.034 / 2

or,

Distance to object (in cm) = (time to received echo in µs) * 0.017

Figure 7.59 shows the principle of operation of the ultrasonic sensor module. For example, if the time to receive the echo is 294 microseconds then the distance to the object is calculated as:

Distance to object (cm) = 294 * 0.017 = 5cm

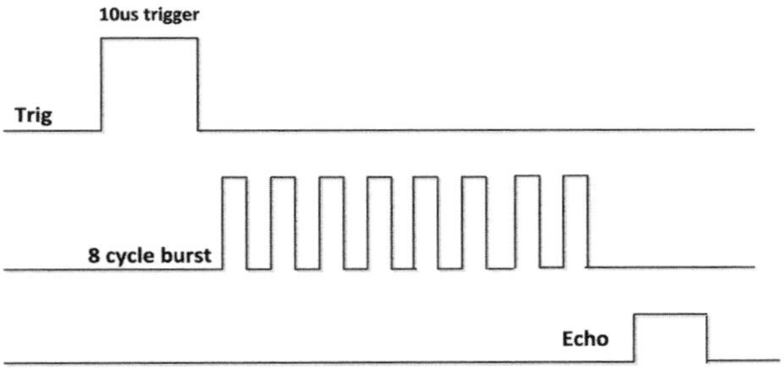

Figure 7.59 Operation of the ultrasonic sensor module

Figure 7.60 shows the circuit diagram of the project. The trig and echo pins of the Front ultrasonic sensor are connected to GPIO 2 and GPIO 3 respectively. Similarly, trig and echo pins of the Read ultrasonic sensor are connected to GPIO 4 and GPIO 17 respectively. Echo outputs of the ultrasonic sensors are connected to the Raspberry Pi through potential divider resistors to drop the voltage levels to +3.3V. The buzzer is connected to GPIO 27 of the Raspberry Pi.

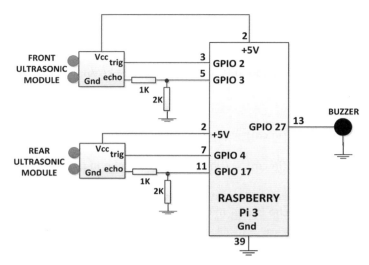

Figure 7.60 Circuit diagram of the project

Program listing: Figure 7.61 shows the program listing (program **parking.py**). The front sensor pins are named **trig_f** and **echo_f**. Similarly, the rear sensor pins are named as **trig_r** and **echo_r**. The distances from both sensors to obstacles are measured using function **GetDistance,** where the **trig** and **echo** pin names of the sensor whose distance to the obstacles is to be measured. A 10 microsecond trigger pulse is sent and then the time taken to receive the echo pulse is measured. Here, the **time.time()** function is used after sending the trigger pulse and the same function is used as soon as the echo pulse is received. The difference between the two times is the time taken to receive the echo pulse. This time is divided by 2 and the distance to the object is found in cm as follows:

> Speed of sound = 340 m/s, or 34000cm/s
> Distance to object (cm) = 34000 x time / 2

where, time is in seconds and it is the time taken to receive the echo pulse. We can re-write the above equation as:

> Distance to object (cm) = 17000 x time

If the distances of either sensors to the objects is less than or equal to the **Allowed_Distance** (which is set to 10cm) then the buzzer is sounded to indicate that the vehicle is too close to objects (either at the front or at the rear).

Since the parking sensor is to be operated away from a PC it is necessary to auto start the program when power is applied to the Raspberry Pi. The program name **parking.py** must be included in file **/etc/rc.local** in the following format so that the program starts as soon as the Raspberry Pi starts after a power-up or after a reboot:

python /home/pi/robot2.py &

```
#------------------------------------------------------------------
#                         PARKING SENSORS
#                         ===============
#
# This is a parking sensors project. Ultrasonic tranamitter/receiver
# sensors are attached to the front and rear of a vehicle. In addition
# an active buzzer is connected to the Raspberry Pi. The program senses
# the objects in the front and rear of the vehicle and sounds the buzzer
# if the vehicle is too close to the objects. In this project a distance
# less than 10cm is considered to be too close.
#
#
# File   : parking.py
# Date   : October 2017
# Author: Dogan Ibrahim
#------------------------------------------------------------------
import RPi.GPIO as GPIO
import time
GPIO.setwarnings(False)
GPIO.setmode(GPIO.BCM)
Allowed_Distance = 10           # Distance in cm

#
# Front Ultrasonic sensor pins
#
trig_f = 2                      # GPIO 2
echo_f = 3                      # GPIO 3

#
# Rear ultrasonic sensor pins
#
trig_r = 4                      # GPIO 4
echo_r = 17                     # GPIO 17

#
# BUZZER pin
#
Buzzer = 27                     # GPIO 27

#
# Configure trig and buzzer as outputs, echos as inputs
#
GPIO.setup(trig_f, GPIO.OUT)
GPIO.setup(trig_r, GPIO.OUT)
```

```
GPIO.setup(echo_f, GPIO.IN)
GPIO.setup(echo_r, GPIO.IN)
GPIO.setup(Buzzer, GPIO.OUT)

#
# Turn ON the Buzzer
#
def BUZZERON():
  GPIO.output(Buzzer, 1)
  return

#
# Turn OFF the Buzzer
#
def BUZZEROFF():
  GPIO.output(Buzzer, 0)
  return

def GetDistance(trig, echo):
  GPIO.output(trig, 0)                      # Wait to settle
  time.sleep(0.08)
  GPIO.output(trig,1)                       # Send trig
  time.sleep(0.00001)                       # Wait 10 microseconds
  GPIO.output(trig, 0)                      # Remove trig
  while GPIO.input(echo) == 0:              # Wait until echo is received
    start_time = time.time()               # Start time

  while GPIO.input(echo) == 1:             # Echo is received
    end_time = time.time()                 # End time

  pulse_width = end_time - start_time       # Pulse duration
  distance = pulse_width * 17150            # Distance in cm
  return distance                           # Return distance

#
# Start of the main program loop. Measure the distance to obstacles
# at the front and rear of the vehicle and activate the buzzer if the
# distance is below the allowed distance
#
BUZZEROFF()

while True:
  obstacle_f = GetDistance(trig_f, echo_f) # distance to front obstacles
  obstacle_r = GetDistance(trig_r, echo_r) # distance to rear obstacles
  if (obstacle_f or obstacle_r) <= Allowed_Distance:
    BUZZERON()                              # Turn Buzzer ON
```

```
else:
    BUZZEROFF()                                    # Turn Buzzer OFF
```

Figure 7.61 Program listing

After applying power, wait until the Raspberry Pi boots and the program should start automatically. You should remove your Python program name from file **/etc/rc.local** after testing and completing your project so that the program does not start every time you restart your Raspberry Pi.

7.14 Summary

In this Chapter we have seen the design of simple projects consisting of LEDs, buzzers, push button switches, ultrasonic sensors and so on.

In next Chapter we shall see how to plot real-time graphs using the Raspberry Pi with Python.

CHAPTER 8 • PLOTTING REAL-TIME GRAPHS

8.1 Overview
In this Chapter we shall see how to write programs using Python to draw real-time graphs of the data received by the Raspberry Pi. The ambient temperature and humidity are read and their graphs drawn in real-time as the data is generated.

Before going into the details of the project, it is worthwhile to see how graphs can be drawn using Python on the Raspberry Pi.

8.2 Plotting in Python
Plotting graphs in Python is very easy with the **matplotlib** module. This module enables us to plot offline as well as real-time graphs. In this section it is explained how to draw graphs offline to make the user familiar with the functions of the **matplotlib** module. Real-time plotting is described in a later section.

The **matplotlib** library module must be installed in Python before it can be used. This is done in command mode by entering the following command:

pi@raspberrypi~ $ **sudo apt-get install python-matplotlib**

8.2.1 Graph of a Quadratic Function
As an example, the graph of the quadratic function $y = x^2$ is drawn in this section using Python. At the beginning of the program **matplotlib** module and the **numpy** modules are imported into Python. **numpy** is a scientific package including many mathematical functions that can be used in Python programs.

The graphics can only be drawn in GUI Desktop mode. You should therefore use the VNC Viewer to get into the GUI mode and then create and run your program from there by selecting **Python 2 (IDLE).** The program listing is as follows:

```
import matplotlib.pyplot as plt
import numpy as np
x = np.linspace(0,4,100)
plt.plot(x, x**2)
plt.show()
```

Figure 8.1 shows the graph plotted. Function **linspace(0,4,100)** creates a list 100 integer numbers in **x**, starting from 0 and terminating at 4. Function **plot** draws the graph where the **y** value is equal to **x^2** . Function **show()** physically displays the graph. Notice that there are some buttons at the bottom of the window. These buttons are (from left to right as shown in Figure 8.2):

Home: Clicking this button displays the default figure as in Figure 8.1
Back: Brings back the plot after zooming
Next: This button is opposite of Back button

Pan: This button moves the window coordinates
Zoom: This button selects a zoom window
Adjust: this button adjusts the plot parameters
Save: click to save the plot

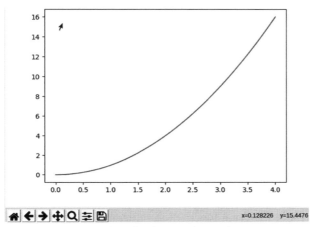

Figure 8.1 Graph of a quadratic function

Figure 8.2 Graph buttons

The graph is Figure 8.1 can be made more user friendly by labelling the axes and giving a title to the graph. The modified program is given below:

```
import matplotlib.pyplot as plt
import numpy as np
x = np.linspace(0,4,100)
plt.plot(x, x**2, label='Quadratic')
plt.xlabel('X values')
plt.ylabel('Y values')
plt.title('Graph of y = x**2')
plt.legend()
plt.show()
```

The new graph is shown in Figure 8.3.

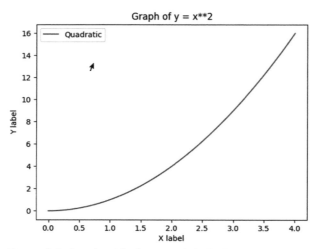

Figure 8.3 Graph with the axes labelled and with a title

8.2.2 Drawing Multiple Graphs

We can easily plot more than one function on the same graph. In the example code given below three graphs are drawn on the same axes: graph of y = x+5, y = x² , and y = x***3:

```
import matplotlib.pyplot as plt
import numpy as np
x = np.linspace(0,4,100)
plt.plot(x, x+5,label='x+5')
plt.plot(x, x**2, label='Quadratic')
plt.plot(x, x**3,label='Cubic')
plt.xlabel('X values')
plt.ylabel('Y values')
plt.title('Graphs of linear,quadratic,and cubic functions')
plt.legend()
plt.show()
```

Figure 8.4 shows the graph with three functions.

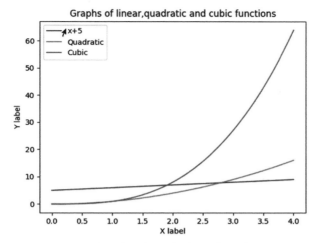

Figure 8.4 Graph with three functions

Function plot draws a smooth graph by joining the x,y values. We can also draw different types of graph. For example, function **scatter** draws a scatter graph as shown in Figure 8.5. The program for this graph is as follows:

```
import matplotlib.pyplot as plt
import numpy as np
x = np.linspace(0,4,100)
plt.scatter(x, x+5,label='x+5')
plt.scatter(x, x**2, label='Quadratic')
plt.scatter(x, x**3,label='Cubic')
plt.xlabel('X values')
plt.ylabel('Y values')
plt.title('Graphs of linear,quadratic,and cubic functions')
plt.legend()
plt.show()
```

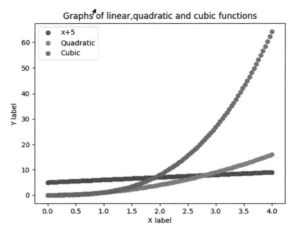

Figure 8.5 Drawing a scatter graph

Function bar draws a bar chart as shown in Figure 8.6. The program for this graps is as follows:

```
import matplotlib.pyplot as plt
import numpy as np
x = np.linspace(0,4,100)
plt.bar(x, x+5,label='x+5')
plt.bar(x, x**2, label='Quadratic')
plt.bar(x, x**3,label='Cubic')
plt.xlabel('X values')
plt.ylabel('Y values')
plt.title('Graphs of linear,quadratic,and cubic functions')
plt.legend()
plt.show()
```

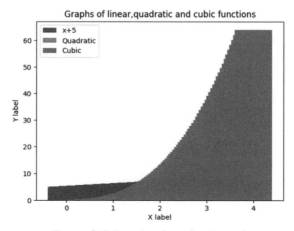

Figure 8.6 Drawing bar chart graph

matplotlib is a large graphics library with many functions and the details of these functions are beyond the scope of this book. Interested readers can find books, tutorials, and applications notes on **matplotlib** on the Internet (e.g. https://matplotlib.org/faq/usage_faq.html).

8.3 PROJECT - Real-Time Graph of the Temperature and Humidity
What we are really interested in is to plot graphs in real-time as the data is being generated. By default, the real-time plotting option is turned OFF and it can be turned ON by the statement: **plt.ion()**.

Description: In this project we will read the temperature and the humidity using a sensor with the Raspberry Pi 3 and then plot the change in the temperature and humidity in real-time as the data is captured continuously. The details of this project are given in this section.

Aim: The aim of this project is to show how a sensor data captured by the Raspberry Pi can be plotted in real-time. The project also shows how to use a temperature and humidity sensor with the Raspberry Pi 3.

Raspberry Pi Type: This project will run on all types of Raspberry Pi.

Block diagram: The block diagram of the project is shown in Figure 8.7.

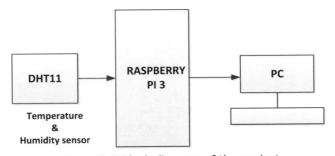

Figure 8.7 Block diagram of the project

Circuit diagram: A DHT11 type temperature and humidity sensor chip (see Figure 8.8) is used in this project. This is normally a 3-pin sensor (there is also a 4-pin version of this sensor where one of the pins is not used) with pins GND, +V, and Data. GND and +V are connected to the ground and the +3.3V power supply pins of the Raspberry Pi. The Data pin must be connected to +V through a 10K resistor. In this project a 3-pin DHT11 from Elektor is used with built-in 10K pull-up resistor. As shown in Figure 8.9, the Data pin of the sensor is named as S and it is connected to GPIO 2 of the Raspberry Pi.

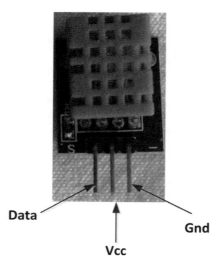

Data

Gnd

Vcc

Figure 8.8 DHT11 sensor

DHT11 uses capacitive humidity sensor and a thermistor to measure the ambient temperature. Data output is available from the chip around every second. The basic features of DHT11 are:

- 3 to 5V operation
- 2.5mA current consumption (during a conversion)
- Temperature reading in the range 0-50ºC with an accuracy of ±2ºC
- Humidity reading in the range 20-80% with 5% accuracy
- Breadboard compatible with 0.1 inch pin spacings

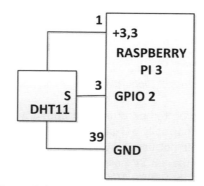

Figure 8.9 Circuit diagram of the project

Construction: The project is constructed on a breadboard as shown in Figure 8.10. Female-male jumper cables are used to connect the sensor to the GPIO port and to the GND and power supply pins.

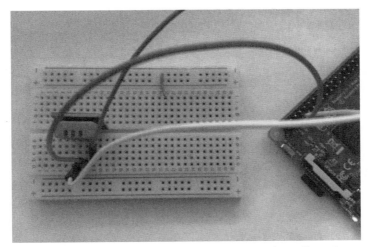

Figure 8.10 Constructing the project on a breadboard

Program listing: In this program the Adafruit DHT11 library module is used. This module should be installed into Python before it can be used. The instructions for this are as follows:

Go to command mode and enter:

> pi@raspberrypi~ $ **git clone https://github.com/adafruit/Adafruit_ Python_DHT.git**

Change directory to:

> cd Adafruit_Python_DHT

Enter the following commands:

> sudo apt-get install build-essential python-dev

> sudo python setup.py install

Figure 8.11 shows the program listing (program: **graph.py**). At the beginning of the program the **matplotlib, numpy, time**, and **Adafruit** modules are imported to the program. Sensor type (variable **sensor**) is set to be DHT11, and it is connected to port GPIO 2. Then the X-axis is defined to run from 0 to 100 seconds, and the Y-axis to run from 0 to 100 (the temperature or the humidity cannot be greater than 100). X and Y axes are labelled and also a title is given to the graph. The graph is set to be interactive by the statement **ion().** The remainder of the program runs in a **for** loop which executes as variable **i** changed from 0 to 100 in steps of 2, and this corresponds to the time axis (the length of the data collection time and hence the length of the X-axis can be changed if desired). The humidity and temperature are then read from the DHT11 and stored in variables **humidity** and **temperature** respectively. These values are then formatted into simple numeric data and are stored in variables **t** and **h,** ready to be plotted. Scatter graphs are then drawn in real-time as the temperature and humidity data are received from the DHT11. Two seconds of delay is introduced between each loop.

```
#-----------------------------------------------------------------
#
#            REAL TIME GRAPH OF HUMIDITY AND TEMPERATURE
#            ===========================================
#
# This program reads the ambient temperature and himidity from
# a DHT11 type sensor and displays them on the monitor in real-time
# as a graph.
#
# In this program data is collected every 2 seconds, for a period
# of 100 seconds.
#
#
# Program: graph.py
# Date    : October 2017
# Author : Dogan Ibrahim
#-----------------------------------------------------------------
import matplotlib
matplotlib.use('TkAgg')
import matplotlib.pyplot as plt
import numpy as np
import time
import Adafruit_DHT

sensor = Adafruit_DHT.DHT11
GPIO = 2


#
# Start of main program. Humidity and temperature are read from
# DHT11 and are plotted in real time as the data are being read
#
plt.axis([0,100,0,100])
plt.title('Humidity and Temperature')
plt.xlabel('Time')
plt.ylabel('Hum. & Temp')

j=1
plt.ion()


#
# Read the humidity and temperature every 2 seconds for 100 seconds
#
```

```
for i in range (0,102,2):
    humidity,temperature = Adafruit_DHT.read_retry(sensor,GPIO)
    x = float(i)
    t = '{0:0.1f}'.format(temperature)
    h = '{0:0.1f}'.format(humidity)
    plt.scatter(x,t,color='blue',label='Tempeature')
    plt.scatter(x,h,color='black',label='Humidity')
    plt.draw()
    if j == 1:
        j=0
        plt.legend()
    plt.pause(0.0001)
    time.sleep(2)
```

Figure 8.11 Program listing

The real-time change of the temperature and humidity are shown in Figure 8.12. In this figure the top graph is the humidity and the bottom one is the temperature.

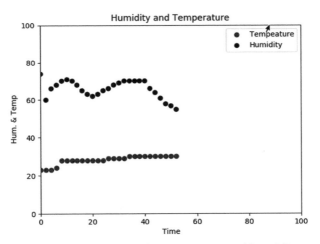

Figure 8.12 Change of temperature and humidity

8.4 Summary
In this Chapter we have seen how to draw graphs using the Puthon library matplotlib. A project is also given where the ambient temperature and humidity are read from a sensor and are plotted in real-time as the data is received.

In the next Chapter we shall see how to use the **pygame** module to display the temperature and humidity.

CHAPTER 9 • USING THE PYGAME TO DISPLAY THE HUMIDITY AND TEMPERATURE

9.1 Overview

In last Chapter we have seen how to use the **matplotlib** library to plot the graph of the ambient humidity and temperature in real-time. In this Chapter we will be seeing how to display the change of the ambient humidity and temperature using the **pygame** library.

9.2 Pygame

Pygame is an animation library used mainly for games programming. Pygame library functions can be used to draw any kind of shape with the required colour. In addition, there are many functions to move and rotate shapes, handle keyboard and mouse inputs, handle various other external and internal events, and many more functions. In this Chapter we shall be looking at the very basic functions of the pygame to draw a box and then display the humidity and the temperature inside this box in the form of an animation as the humidity or the temperature change.

Pygame is a very large library and there are many books, tutorials, application notes, and example programs on the Internet, teaching how to use the pygame. The details of pygame are beyond the scope of this book, and this Chapter is aimed to teach the very basics of pygame. Interested readers should refer to the Internet for detailed information on pygame.

Notice that you must run the pygame programs from the GUI Desktop environment after running the VCN server on the Raspberry Pi in command mode, and then logging in using the VCN Viewer.

9.3 Drawing a Shape

9.3.1 Rectangle

Perhaps the easiest shape to draw using pygame is a rectangle. The example code shown below draws a rectangle:

```
import pygame
pygame.init()
window = pygame.display.set_mode((600, 500))
while True:
    pygame.draw.rect(window, (255, 0, 0), (100, 150, 80, 50))
    pygame.display.update()
```

At the beginning of the code pygame library is imported and then pygame is initialized. Then, a window is defined having 600 horizontal pixels (width) and 500 vertical pixels (height). After defining the window size we can draw our shapes inside. The **draw.rect** statement draws a rectangle. The colour of the rectangle is first defined, where (255, 0, 0) corresponds to red colour (RED, GREEN, BLUE). The first two parameters in (100, 150, 80, 50) define where the rectangle will be placed inside the window. The first parameter is the

X coordinate of the left edge of the rectangle. Second parameter is the Y coordinate of the top edge of the rectangle. The last two parameters 50,30 define the width and height of the rectangle in pixels. Statement **display.update()** updates the display.

Figure 9.1 shows the window and the rectangle drawn inside this window.

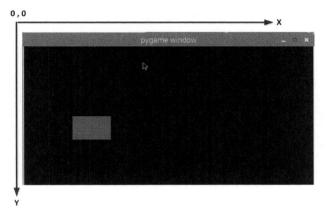

Figure 9.1 Drawing a window and a rectangle

9.3.2 Circle
Drawing a circle is similar. An example code is given below, where as with the rectangle, (255, 255, 255) is the colour of the circle (white here), next two parameters (100, 150) is the center of the circle as (X, Y), next parameter 40 is the radius in pixels, and the last parameter 2 is the width of the circle:

```
import pygame
pygame.init()
window = pygame.display.set_mode((600, 500))
while True:
    pygame.draw.circ(window, (255, 255, 255), (100, 150), 40, 2)
    pygame.display.update()
```

Figure 9.2 shows the window and the circle drawn inside this window.

Figure 9.2 Drawing a window and a circle

9.4 PROJECT - Real-Time Graph of the Temperature and Humidity

What we are really interested in is to display the humidity and the temperature using a pygame window.

Description: In this project we will read the temperature and the humidity using a sensor with the Raspberry Pi 3 as in the previous project, and then display the change in the temperature and humidity in real-time as the data is read continuously. The details of this project are given in this section.

Aim: The aim of this project is to show how the sensor data captured by the Raspberry Pi can be displayed in a pygame window in real-time.

Raspberry Pi Type: This project will run on all types of Raspberry Pi.

Block diagram: The block diagram of the project is as in Figure 8.7.

Circuit diagram: The circuit diagram of the project is as in Figure 8.9.

Construction: The project is constructed on a breadboard as shown in Figure 8.10.

Program listing: Figure 9.3 shows the program listing (program: **pygme.py**). At the beginning of the program the **time**, **pygame**, **sys**, and **Adafruit** modules are imported to the program. Sensor type (variable **sensor**) is set to be DHT11, and it is connected to port GPIO 2. The program the initializes pygame and defines the window coordinates as 800x600 pixels. A font is chosen for the text and title **Temperature and Humidity** is displayed at the top of the window. The remainder of the program is executed in a **while** loop. Inside the loop the program checks for pygame events and if the program is terminated (by clicking the little cross sign at the top right hand corner of the screen) the program terminates.

The humidity and temperature are read from the DHT11 and are converted into integer numbers and are stored in variables **h** and **t** respectively. Two rectangular windows are then drawn, one for the temperature display and one for the humidity display. The temperature rectangle is red colour and starts from X coordinate 100 pixels (gap), while its Y coordinate is 0 (i.e. level with the top of the window). The humidity rectangle is black colour and starts from X coordinate 500 pixels (gap+w2), while its Y coordinate is also 0. The width of both windows is 200 pixels (w/4). The height of the windows is set to be the value measured times 6 pixels. Therefore, as the values read from the sensors change so does the heights of the rectangles. The program then displays the actual values read from the sensors in the middle bottom parts of the rectangles. The values are displayed in white colour. The temperature value is displayed at coordinate (gap+45, 5), i.e. at X = 145 and Y = 5. The humidity is displayed at coordinate (w2+gap+45, 5), i.e. at X = 545 and Y = 5. The display is updated every 2 seconds. This is because the recommended update interval of the DHT11 sensor is no more than every 2 seconds.

```
#----------------------------------------------------------------
#
#          REAL TIME DISPLAY OF HUMIDITY AND TEMPERATURE
#          ==============================================
#
# This program reads the ambient temperature and humidity from
# a DHT11 type sensor and then displays them on the monitor in
# real-time in a pygame window.
#
# The sensor is connected to GPIO 2
#
#
# Program: pygme.py
# Date    : October 2017
# Author : Dogan Ibrahim
#----------------------------------------------------------------
import pygame
import time
import sys
import Adafruit_DHT

sensor = Adafruit_DHT.DHT11
GPIO = 2

#
# Colours
#
black = (0, 0, 0)
red = (255, 0, 0)
white = (255, 255, 255)

pygame.init()
width = 800
height = 600
w2 = width / 2
w4 = width / 4

window = pygame.display.set_mode((width, height))
fontused=pygame.font.SysFont("comicsansms",50)
pygame.display.set_caption('Temperature and Humidity')
gap = width/8

#
# Start of main program. Humidity and temperature are read from
# DHT11 and displayed in a pygame window. Exit the program if
# the QUIT (window close cross sign) is clicked
```

```
#
while True:
    for event in pygame.event.get():
        if event.type == pygame.QUIT:
            sys.exit()
#
# Read humidity and temperature
#
    humidity,temperature = Adafruit_DHT.read_retry(sensor,GPIO)
    t = int(temperature)
    h = int(humidity)
#
# Make window white and draw rectangles for humidity and temp
#
    window.fill(white)
    pygame.draw.rect(window, red, (gap, 0, w4, t*6))
    pygame.draw.rect(window, black, (w2+gap, 0, w4, h*6))
#
# Insert labels with the values of humidity and temperature
#
    left_label = fontused.render(str(t)+"C" , 1, white)
    window.blit(left_label, (gap+45, 5))
    right_label = fontused.render(str(h)+"%", 1, white)
    window.blit(right_label, (w2+gap+45, 5))
#
# Update
#
    pygame.display.update()
    time.sleep(2)
```

Figure 9.3 Program listing

The real-time change of the temperature and humidity are shown in Figure 9.4.

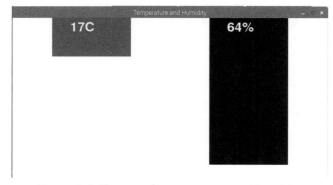

Figure 9.4 Change of temperature and humidity

9.5 Summary

In this Chapter we have seen how to display the ambient humidity and temperature in a pygame window.

In the next Chapter we shall see how to use the Pi 3 Shield in Raspberry Pi 3 based projects.

CHAPTER 10 • USING THE Pi 3 CLICK SHIELD

10.1 Overview
In this Chapter we shall see how to use the Pi 3 Click Shield in Raspberry Pi 3 projects. The basic features of this shield as well as its use in Raspberry Pi 3 projects with the Python programming language will be explained with a simple project.

10.2 The Pi 3 Click Shield
Pi 3 Click Shield (Figure 10.1) is a small board manufactured by mikroElektronika (www.mikroe.com). The board has the following basic features:

- Plug-in on top of the Raspberry Pi 3 board
- 2 mikroBUS sockets
- On-board 12-bit ADC with switch selector
- Voltage translator (5V to 3.3V)

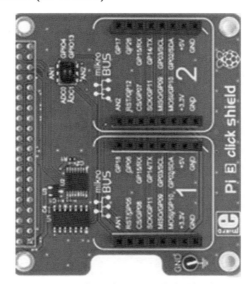

Figure 10.1 The Pi 3 Click Shield

mikroBUS (see Figure 10.2) is a 16-pin bus specification that has been developed by mikro-Elektronika. Many companies have developed mikroBUS compatible **Click Boards** that can be plugged-in and used with boards that have mikroBUS sockets. There are over 200 mikroBUS compatible sensors, actuators, displays, relays and many other components. Thus, using the Pi 3 Click Shield board allows us to have access to over 200 click boards in our Raspberry Pi 3 projects.

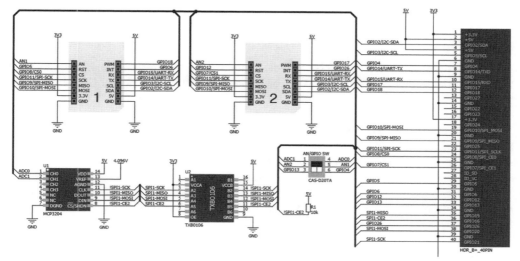

Figure 10.2 Standard mikroBUS specification

The ADC on-board is the MCP3204 4-channel 12-bit chip, with a reference voltage of 4.096V. Only two analog inputs (ADC0 abd ADC1) are used on the board. The ADC works with 5V and thus a voltage translator chip (TXB0106) is used to convert voltages to 3.3V so that they are compatible with the raspberry Pi. A small switch is provided on the Pi 3 Click Shield that can be used to select between the two ADC inputs or the standard GPIO inputs. The GPIO inputs that can be selected with this switch are GPIO4 and GPIO13. The ADC provided by this shield could be useful since the Raspberry Pi 3 has no analog input pins.

The two mikroBUS sockets on the Pi 3 Shield has the following pin configurations:

SOCKET 1

AN1	GP18
RST/GP05	GP06
CS/GP08	GP15/RX
SCK/GP11	GP14/TX
MISO/GP09	GP03/SCL
+3.3V	+5V
GND	GND

SOCKET 2

AN2	GP17
RST/GP12	GP26
CS/GP07	GP15/RX
SCK/GP11	GP14/TX
MISO/GP09	GP03/SCL
MOSI/GP10	GP02/SDA

+3.3V	+5V
GND	GND

AN1 and AN2 on sockets 1 and 2 respectively can either be selected by the on-board switch to be the analog inputs ADC0 and ADC1 or the digital inputs GPIO4 and GPIO13 respectively.

10.3 PROJECT – USING A 7-SEGMENT DISPLAY CLICK BOARD

Description: In this project we will be using a dual 7-segment display to count up every second from 0 to 99 repeatedly. The UT-M 7-SEG R Click Board (www.mikroe.com) is used in this project together with the Pi 3 Click Shield.

Aim: The aim of this project is to show how the Pi 3 Click Shield can be used in Raspberry Pi 3 projects.

Raspberry Pi Type: This project will run on the Raspberry Pi 3.

Block Diagram: The block diagram of the project is shown in Figure 10.3. The UT-M 7-SEG R Click board has two 7-segment red colour displays on-board. The two displays are controlled from a MAX6969 chip. Interface to this click board is through the SPI bus

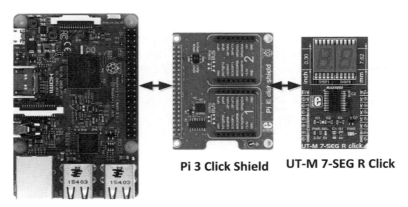

Pi 3 Click Shield   **UT-M 7-SEG R Click**

RASPBERRY PI 3

Figure 10.3 Block diagram of the project

When the UT-M 7-SEG R click board is plugged-in on top of the Pi 3 Click Shield, the following pins are connected together:

MAX6969 OE pin to GPIO18
MAX6969 LE pin to GPIO8
Display SCK pin to SCK (GPIO11)
Display SDO pin to MISO (GPIO9)
Display SDI pin to MOSI (GPIO10)

Figure 10.4 shows the circuit diagram of the Pi 3 Click Shield board. The UT-M 7-SEG R click board is shown in Figure 10.5.

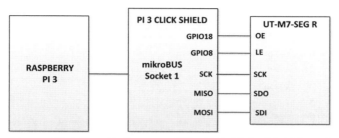

Figure 10.4 Circuit diagram of the Pi 3 Click Shield board

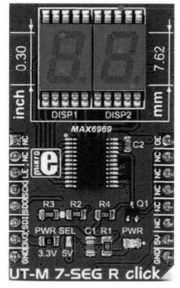

Figure 10.5 The UT-M 7-SEg R click board

Program: Figure 10.6 shows the program listing (program: shield.py). At the beginning of the program modules time, spidev, and RPi.GPIO are imported to the program. MAX6969 pins LE and OE are then defined and they are configured as outputs. Function **Chip_Select** activated the chip. Function **UTM_Write** receives variable **number** as its parameter and extracts the MSB and the LSB digits of the number and then sends them to the display. Inside the program loop the value of variable **count** is incremented by 1 and is then displayed every second, thus the display shows incrementing numbers from 00 to 99.

```
#-------------------------------------------------------------
#
#               Pi 3 CLICK SHIELD 7-SEG DISPLAY
#               ================================
#
```

```
# In this project the Pi 3 Click Shield is connected to the
# Raspberry Pi 3. In addition, the UT-M 7-SEG R click is
# connected to this Shield. The project counts up by one every
# second from 0 to 99 and displays on the 7-Seg display
#
# Author: Dogan Ibrahim
# Date   : December, 2017
# File   : shield.py
#-------------------------------------------------------------
import spidev
import time
import RPi.GPIO as GPIO
GPIO.setmode(GPIO.BCM)
GPIO.setwarnings(False)


#
# Create SPI instance and open the SPI bus
#
spi = spidev.SpiDev()
spi.open(0, 1)


#
# Define MAC6969 pins. GPIO 8 is conected to LE pin and
# GPIO 18 is connected to the OE pin
#
MAX6969_LE = 8          # GPIO 8
MAX6969_OE = 18          # GPIO 18


#
# Configure MAX6969_LE and MAX6969_OE as outputs
#
GPIO.setup(MAX6969_LE, GPIO.OUT)
GPIO.setup(MAX6969_OE, GPIO.OUT)

GPIO.output(MAX6969_OE, 1)       # enable chip


#
# MAX6979 Chip Select
#
def MAX6969_Chip_Select():
  GPIO.output(MAX6969_LE, 1)
  time.sleep(0.000001)
  GPIO.output(MAX6969_LE, 0)


#
# UT-M 7-Seg Click write. Send the LSB and the MSB digits
```

```
# to the display
#
def UTM_Write(number):
  numbers = (0x3F,0x06,0x5B,0x4F,0x66,0x6D,0x7D,0x07,0x7F,0x6F)
  msb = number / 10
  lsb = number % 10
  spi.xfer([numbers[lsb], numbers[msb]])


#
# Program loop. Here, variable counter is incremented by one
# every second and sent to the display. The display shows the
# count in 2 digits from 00 to 99
#
count = 1

while True:
  UTM_Write(count)              # write to display
  MAX6969_Chip_Select()         # chip select
  count = count + 1             # increment count
  if count > 99:                # if 99, reset to 0
    count = 0
  time.sleep(1)                 # wait 1 second
```

Figure 10.6 Program listing

Figure 10.7 shows the project assembly with the Pi 3 Click Shield and the UT-M 7-SEG R click boards connected together.

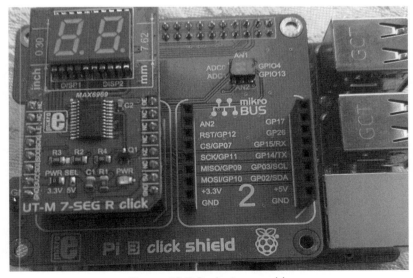

Figure 10.7 Project assembly

10.4 Summary

In this Chapter we have seen how to use the Pi 3 Click Shield. Next Chapter is about using the popular Sense HAT board in Raspberry Pi 3 projects.

CHAPTER 11 • USING THE Sense HAT

11.1 Overview
The Sense HAT is an add-on board for the Raspberry Pi containing a number of useful sensors and an LED array. HAT is an acronym for **H**ardware **A**ttached on **T**op. Sense HAT was an important component of the Astro Pi project, which was an educational Raspberry Pi sent to the International Space Station with the British astronaut Tim Peake to run code developed by children. The actual Astro Pi had some modifications and had metal casing to make it suitable for use in space.

Sense HAT includes sensors to measure temperature, humidity, pressure, accelerometer, gyroscope, and a magnetometer. In addition, an 8 x 8 independently programmable LED array is included on the board that can be programmed to display text and small images. In this Chapter we shall be designing various projects using the Sense HAT board. But before that it is worthwhile to look at the features of the Sense HAT board. Detailed information on Sense HAT can be obtained from the link: **magpi.cc/AstroPiGuide**. Also from the **Essentials_SenseHAT_v1** (MagPi Essentials series), and from many other Internet sources.

11.2 The Sense HAT Board
Figure 11.1 shows the Sense HAT board. We can identify the following components on the board:

- 8 x 8 LED array, having 15-bit colour resolution
- One chip containing accelerometer, gyroscope, and magnetometer to measure speed, orientation and the strength and direction of a magnetic field
- One chip containing temperature and humidity sensor
- Barometric pressure sensor chip capable of measuring the pressure exerted by small air molecules
- Graphics controller chip
- Five-button joystick with left, right, up, down, and enter movements

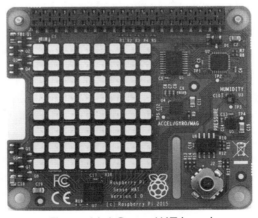

Figure 11.1 Sense HAT board

11.3 Programming the Sense HAT

In order to program the Sense HAT, you should be in the desktop GUI mode. Start your Raspberry Pi in command mode and then start the VCN server. You should then login to the Desktop GUI mode by using the VCN Viewer. You should use the Python 3 (IDLE 3) to program your Sense HAT.

The Sense HAT library must be imported into your Python program and also the **sense** object must be created at the beginning of the program. i.e. the following two statements must be included at the beginning of your programs:

```
from sense_hat import SenseHAT
sense = SenseHat()
```

11.4 Displaying Text on Sense HAT

In this project we shall display the scrolling message **Hello from Sense HAT** on the LED matrix. The required program listing is given below. Notice that the message is displayed only once:

```
from sense_hat import SenseHat
sense = SenseHat()
sense.show_message("Hello from Sense HAT")
```

We can also display a single letter using the statement: **sense.show_letter**, for example, **sense.show_letter("A")**. Notice that the letter is displayed continuously.

In addition to displaying text in default mode, we can use the following options:

scroll_speed: This parameter changes the speed that the text scrolls. The default value is 0.1. A bigger number slows down the scroll speed.

text_colour: Used to change the text colour. The colour is specified as (Red, Green, Blue) where each colour can take a value between 0 and 255. For example, (255, 0, 0) is red and so on.

back_colour: used to change the colour of the background. Colour is defined as in the text_colour option.

In the following example, the same text as above is scrolled slowly, in red colour, with yellow background colour:

```
from sense_hat import SenseHat
sense = SenseHat()
sense.show_message("Hello from Sense HAT", scroll_speed=0.3,
    text_colour=[255,0,0], back_colour=[255,255,0])
```

Notice that in the above program the text is displayed only once, but the background colour remains as yellow. If for example we wish to repeat displaying the text, say every two seconds, then the required program is as follows:

```
from sense_hat import SenseHat
import time
sense = SenseHat()
while True:
    sense.show_message("Hello from Sense HAT", scroll_speed=0.3,
        text_colour=[255,0,0], back_colour=[255,255,0])
    time.sleep(2)
```

We can use the **sense.clear()** statement to clear all the LEDs. This may be necessary to ensure that all the LEDs are turned OFF at the beginning of a program. Similarly, a colour can be passed to the clear statement, such as **sense.clear(red)**.

The brightness of the LED matrix can be changed by toggling the **low_light** statement. In the following examples the brightness is toggled:

```
sense.low_light = True
```
or
```
sense.low_light = False
```

11.5 Displaying Images on Sense HAT

Images can be created on the 8 x 8 LED by individually controlling each LED. The LED matrix has the co-ordinate system shown in Figure 11.2, where (0, 0) is the top left corner of the LED array, and X is the horizontal direction from left to right, while Y is the vertical direction from top to bottom.

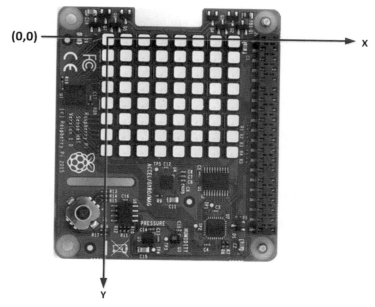

(0,0) →   → X

Y

Figure 11.2 LED coordinates

The statement **sense.set_pixel()** sets the pixels specified inside the bracket together with the required colours. In the following example, the LED at coordinates (0, 3) is set to red, and the LED at coordinate (5, 4) is set to green:

```
from sense_hat import SenseHat
sense = SenseHat()
sense.set_pixel(0, 3, [255, 0 ,0])
sense.set_pixel(5, 4, [0, 255, 0])
```

By giving different colours to the LEDs we can easily create images. In the example below, a smiley face image is created in red colour:

```
from sense_hat import SenseHat
sense = SenseHat()
sense.set_pixel(2, 2, [255,0,0])
sense.set_pixel(4, 2 ,[255,0,0])
sense.set_pixel(3, 4, [255,0,0])
sense.set_pixel(1, 5, [255,0,0])
sense.set_pixel(2, 6, [255,0,0])
sense.set_pixel(3, 6, [255,0,0])
sense.set_pixel(4, 6, [255,0,0])
sense.set_pixel(5, 5, [255,0,0])
```

We can also use the **sense.set_pixels** statement to set many LEDs. In the example below, the main colours Red, Green, Blue are used to set the required LEDs. Here, top LED row is set to red, middle two LED rows are set to green, and the bottom LED row is set to blue (n is used when it is required not to turn ON an LED):

```
from sense_hat import SenseHat
sense = SenseHat()
r = [255, 0 , 0]
g = [0, 255, 0]
b = [0, 0, 255]
n = [0, 0, 0]
my_image =  [r, r, r, r, r, r, r, r,
             n, n, n, n, n, n, n, n,
             n, n, n, n, n, n, n, n,
             g, g, g, g, g, g, g, g,
             g, g, g, g, g, g, g, g,
             n, n, n, n, n, n, n, n,
             n, n, n, n, n, n, n, n,
             b, b, b, b, b, b, b, b]
sense.set_pixels(my_image)
```

The following example code shows how an up pointing red coloured arrow image can be created:

```
from sense_hat import SenseHat
sense = SenseHat()
r = [255, 0 , 0]
n = [0, 0, 0]
my_image = [n, n, n, r, n, n, n, n,
            n, n,  r, r, r, n, n, n,
            n, r,  n, r, n, r, n, n,
            n, n, n, r, n, n, n, n,
            n, n, n, r, n, n, n, n,
            n, n, n, r, n, n, n, n,
            n, n, n, r, n, n, n, n,
            n, n, n, r, n, n, n, n]
sense.set_pixels(my_image)
```

The **get_pixels** statement can be used to read the pixels into a list containing 64 smaller list of R,G,B pixels, representing the currently displayed image. Similarly, the statement **get_pixel** will return the pixel information at a given coordinate. For example the statement:

```
MyPixel = sense.get_pixel(0, 0)
```

will return the pixel settings at coordinate (0, 0).

The image displayed on the LED matrix can be flipped horizontally or vertically using the statements:

sense.flip_h() for horizontal flip and **sense.flip_v()** for vertical flip.

For example, we can flip (move) the arrow image horizontally with the following codes:

```
from sense_hat import SenseHat
sense = SenseHat()
r = [255, 0 , 0]
n = [0, 0, 0]
my_image = [n, n, n, r, n, n, n, n,
            n, n,  r, r, r, n, n, n,
            n, r,  n, r, n, r, n, n,
            n, n, n, r, n, n, n, n,
            n, n, n, r, n, n, n, n,
            n, n, n, r, n, n, n, n,
            n, n, n, r, n, n, n, n,
            n, n, n, r, n, n, n, n]
sense.set_pixels(my_image)
sense.flip_h()
```

Another option is to rotate the image through 0°, 90°, 180°, or 270° . For example, to rotate the image by 90 degrees, use the statement **sense.set_rotation(90).** As an example, we can rotate the image above by 90 degrees in a loop every second so that the direction of the arrow changes continuously:

```
from sense_hat import SenseHat
import time
sense = SenseHat()
r = [255, 0 , 0]
n = [0, 0, 0]
my_image = [n, n, n, r, n, n, n, n,
            n, n,  r, r, r, n, n, n,
            n, r,  n, r, n, r, n, n,
            n, n, n, r, n, n, n, n,
            n, n, n, r, n, n, n, n,
            n, n, n, r, n, n, n, n,
            n, n, n, r, n, n, n, n,
            n, n, n, r, n, n, n, n]
sense.set_pixels(my_image)
rot = 0
while True:
        rot = rot + 90
        if rot == 360:
            rot = 0
```

```
sense.set_rotation(rot)
time.sleep(1)
```

Figure 11.3 shows the arrow displayed on the Sense HAT.

Figure 11.3 Displaying an arrow shape on the Sense HAT

11.6 Reading the Temperature, Pressure, and Humidity

The following statements can be used to read the ambient temperature, pressure, and the humidity:

```
Temp = sense.get_temperature()        - temperature in degrees C
Pressure = sense.get_pressure()       - pressure in millibars
Humidity = sense.get_humidity()       - relative humidity as %
```

The temperature, humidity, and pressure readings can contain several digits after the decimal point. In many applications we may want to round the readings to integers or to one or two decimal places.

By default, the statement get_temperature reads the temperature from the humidity sensor. Notice that it is also possible to read the temperature from the pressure sensor:

or, to read the temperature from the pressure sensor:

```
Temp = sense.get_temperature_from_pressure()
```

In the following program the ambient temperature, humidity, and pressure are read and displayed on the monitor every second:

```
from sense_hat import SenseHat
import time
sense = SenseHat()
while True:
    T = sense.get_temperature()
    H = sense.get_humidity()
    P = sense.get_pressure()
    print("Temperature: %s, Humidity: %s, Pressure:%s" %(T,H,P))
    time.sleep(1)
```

Figure 11.4 shows the output of the program.

```
Temperature: 25.0324363708,Humidity: 42.6796798706, Pressure: 997.669677734
Temperature: 24.9414024353,Humidity: 43.2469673157, Pressure: 997.675537109
Temperature: 24.9778156281,Humidity: 43.1847038269, Pressure: 997.656005859
Temperature: 25.0142288208,Humidity: 43.5582809448, Pressure: 997.68359375
Temperature: 25.0324363708,Humidity: 43.001373291, Pressure: 997.670166016
Temperature: 24.9049873352,Humidity: 43.319606781, Pressure: 997.701171875
Temperature: 24.959608078,Humidity: 43.4026260376, Pressure: 997.677978516
Temperature: 25.0142288208,Humidity: 43.3784103394, Pressure: 997.663574219
```

Figure 11.4 Displaying the temperature, humidity, and pressure

We can round the displayed data for example using the Python **round** function as shown in the following program code. The output of this program is shown in Figure 11.5:

```
from sense_hat import SenseHat
import time
sense = SenseHat()
while True:
    T = sense.get_temperature()
    H = sense.get_humidity()
    P = sense.get_pressure()
    TT = round(T, 1)
    HH = round(H, 1)
    PP = round(P, 1)
    print("Temperature: %s, Humidity: %s, Pressure:%s" %(TT,HH,PP))
    time.sleep(1)
```

```
Temperature: 24.9, Humidity: 43.3, Pressure: 997.8
Temperature: 24.9, Humidity: 43.4, Pressure: 997.8
Temperature: 25.0, Humidity: 43.2, Pressure: 997.8
Temperature: 25.0, Humidity: 43.4, Pressure: 997.8
Temperature: 25.0, Humidity: 43.4, Pressure: 997.8
Temperature: 25.1, Humidity: 43.3, Pressure: 997.9
Temperature: 25.0, Humidity: 43.6, Pressure: 997.8
Temperature: 25.0, Humidity: 43.3, Pressure: 997.9
```

Figure11.5 Rounding the displayed data

We can also display the temperature, humidity and the pressure on the LED matrix. An example program is given below which displays the temperature in red colour every second on the LED matrix. Notice that we have rounded the temperature to one decimal place:

```
from sense_hat import SenseHat
import time
sense = SenseHat()
while True:
    Temp = sense.get_temperature()
    T = round(Temp, 1)
    Txt = "Temperature = %s C" %(T)
    sense.show_message(Txt, text_colour=[255, 0, 0])
    time.sleep(1)
```

11.7 The Inertial Measurement Sensor

The Sense HAT contains an Inertial Measurement Unit (IMU) which is a combination of a compass sensor, gyroscope sensor, and accelerometer sensor. These sensors can be enabled or disabled on an individual basis using the **imu_config** statement. For example, in the following example, all three sensors are enabled:

```
sense.set_imu_config(True, True, True)
```

Similarly, if we wish to enable only the gyroscope sensor, we have to use the statement:

```
sense.set_imu_config(False, True, False)
```

11.7.1 Reading the Compass Direction

The compass direction (with respect to North, where North is 0 degrees, East is 90 degrees, South is 180 degrees, and West is 270 degrees.) can be obtained by the statement **sense. get_compass**. An example is given below which displays the compass direction continuously:

```
from sense_hat import SenseHat
sense = SenseHat()
while True:
    North = sense.get_compass()
    print("North = %s" %North)
```

11.7.2 Reading the Acceleration

We can also get the acceleration (amount of G-force) in three dimensions x, y and z by using the statement:

```
x, y, z = sense.get_accelerometer_raw().values()
```

In the example program below, the acceleration in 3 dimensions is read and displayed continuously. You should run this program and move your Sense HAT in three dimensions and see the acceleration changing in each direction:

```
from sense_hat import SenseHat
sense = SenseHat()
while True:
    x, y, z = sense.get_accelerometer_raw().values()
    print("X=%s, Y=%s, Z=%s" %(x, y, z))
```

11.8 Reading the Orientation (Pitch, Roll, Yaw)

It is important to understand the difference between pitch, roll, and yaw. Perhaps the easiest way to understand these terms is to look at the movements of an aeroplane. Figure 11.6 shows an aeroplane with the terms pitch, roll, and yaw explained graphically.

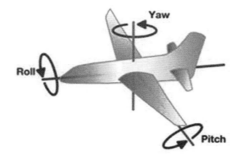

Figure 11.6 Pitch, roll, and yaw of an aeroplane

In Figure 11.7, the terms pitch, roll, and yaw as applied to the Sense HAT is shown.

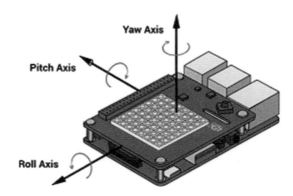

Figure 11.7 Pitch, roll, and yaw of the Sense HAT

The following statement is used to read the pitch, roll and yaw of the Sense HAT, The values are returned in degrees:

```
pitch, roll, yaw = sense.get_orientation().values()
```

In the example program below, the pitch, roll, and yaw are read and displayed on the Python monitor continuously. You should run this program and move your Sense HAT in three dimensions and see the pitch, roll, and yaw changing as the board is moved:

```
from sense_hat import SenseHat
sense = SenseHat()
while True:
    pitch, roll, yaw = sense.get_orientation().values()
    print("pitch=%s, roll=%s, yaw=%s" %(pitch, roll, yaw))
```

By default, the **get_orientation** statement returns the angles in degrees. If we wish to return the angles in radians, we can use the following statement:

```
sense.get_orientation_radians()
```

11.9 Using the Joystick

The joystick is mapped to the for keyboard cursor control keys, with the middle click mapped to the Enter key. With the LED matrix at the top left hand side of the board, there are 5 joystick movements: Up, Down, Left, Right, and clicking in the middle position.

The following functions can be used with the joystick:

InputEvent: This is a tuple that describes a joystick event. It contains three parameters: timestamp, direction, and action. **timestamp** is in fractional number of seconds and it is the time at which the event occurred. **direction** is a string that shows the direction that the joystick was moved It can take the values **up**, **down**, **left**, **right**, and **middle**. **action** is the action that occurred and it can be **pressed**, **released**, or **held**.

wait_for_event: This function waits until a joystick event occurs, and then returns **InputEvent** to show the event type that occurred.

get_events: This function returns a list of **InputEvent** that have occurred since the last call to **get_events** (or to **wait_for_event**).

In the following example, the program waits until a joystick event occurs, and then displays the event:

```
from sense_hat import SenseHat
import time
sense = SenseHat()
while True:
    evnt = sense.stick.wait_for_event()
    print("The event time was: {}, event action was: {}, event direction was:
        {}".format(evnt.timestamp, evnt.action, evnt.direction))
    time.sleep(0.5)
```

Figure 11.8 shows the data printed when the above program is run and the joystick is moved in different directions Notice that in the last display the joystick was pressed.

```
The event time was: 1509125051.39, event action was: released, event direction w
as: up
The event time was: 1509125056.96, event action was: pressed, event direction wa
s: down
The event time was: 1509125057.1, event action was: released, event direction wa
s: down
The event time was: 1509125061.57, event action was: pressed, event direction wa
s: right
The event time was: 1509125061.74, event action was: released, event direction w
as: right
The event time was: 1509125068.0, event action was: pressed, event direction was
: left
The event time was: 1509125068.18, event action was: released, event direction w
as: left
The event time was: 1509125070.89, event action was: pressed, event direction wa
s: middle
```

Figure 11.8 Displaying the joystick movements

We can use the **emptybuffer** keyword to flush any pending events before waiting for a new event. This is shown in the following example:

```
from sense_hat import SenseHat
import time
sense = SenseHat()
while True:
    evnt = sense.stick.wait_for_event()
    print("The event time was: {}, event action was: {}, event direction was:
        {}".format(evnt.timestamp, evnt.action, evnt.direction))
    time.sleep(0.5)
    evnt = sense.stick.wait_for_event(emptybuffer = True)
```

The new display is shown in Figure 11.9 where only one output is displayed when the joystick is moved.

```
The event time was: 1509125387.44, event action was: pressed, event direction wa
s: up
The event time was: 1509125389.58, event action was: released, event direction w
as: right
The event time was: 1509125390.84, event action was: released, event direction w
as: down
The event time was: 1509125392.08, event action was: released, event direction w
as: left
The event time was: 1509125392.98, event action was: released, event direction w
as: middle
```

Figure 11.9 Display after flashing the buffer

We can assign the attributes **direction_up, direction_left, direction_right, direction_down, direction_middle**, and **direction_any** to functions such that these functions will be called when the corresponding joystick events occur. The **direction_any** event is always called after all other events and can be used for example to clear the LED matrix.

An example program code is shown below which calls function **joystick_right** when the joystick is moved in the **right** direction:

```
from sense_hat import SenseHat
from sense_hat import ACTION_RELEASED
        sense = SenseHat()

      def joystick_right(event):
        if event.action != ACTION_RELEASED:
             ............
             ............
             ............


      sense.stick.direction_right = joystick_right
```

11.10 PROJECT 1 – JOYSTICK LED CONTROL

An example program is given in this section to show how the joystick can be used in a program. In this program the LED at coordinate (0, 0) is turned red to start with. Then, using the joystick we move the LED to the right (i.e. turn ON the next LED at its right), to the left, to top, or to bottom by one LED position using the joystick. Notice that when an LED is turned ON the existing LEDs do not turn OFF.

The program listing (joystick.py) is shown in Figure 11.10. At the beginning of the program modules time and SenseHat are imported into the program and the LED at coordinate (0,0) is turned ON in red colour to start with. The remainder of the program runs in an endless loop. Inside this loop the joystick events are detected. If for example, the joystick is moved right then the LED at the right of the current LED is turned ON (if it was not the last LED in that direction). This is checked for all the four directions of the joystick movements.

```
#-------------------------------------------------------------
#                     JOYSTICK LED CONTROL
#                     --------------------
#
# In this project the Sense HAT is connected to the
# Raspberry Pi 3. At the start of the program the LED
# at coordinates (0,0) is turned ON. Then the LEDs are
# turned ON by moving the joystick left, right, top,
# and bottom positions. In this program an LED that is
# turned On stays ON and therefore a pattern can be drawn
# by the LEDs using the joystick. The colour of the LEDs
# are chosen red in this program.
#
# Author: Dogan Ibrahim
# File   : joystick.py
# Date   : November, 2017
#-------------------------------------------------------------
```

```
import time
from sense_hat import SenseHat
sense = SenseHat()

#
# Turn ON the LED at (0,0) to start with
#
x = 0
y = 0

#
# Start of main program loop. Check the joystick events
# and then turn the LEDs ON appropriately
#
while True:
  sense.set_pixel(x, y, [255,0,0])
  for event in sense.stick.get_events():
    if event.action == 'pressed' and event.direction == 'up':
      if y > 0:
        y = y - 1
    if event.action == 'pressed' and event.direction == 'down':
      if y < 7:
        y = y + 1
    if event.action == 'pressed' and event.direction == 'right':
      if x < 7:
        x = x + 1
    if event.action == 'pressed' and event.direction == 'left':
      if x > 0:
        x = x - 1
  time.sleep(0.5)
```

Figure 11.10 Program listing

In Project 1 an LED is turned ON as the joystick is moved, but the existing LEDs do not turn OFF. This program can be modified such that only one LED is ON at any time and the coordinates of this LED changes as the joystick is moved. The modified program (joystick2.py) is shown in Figure 11.11. Here, all the LEDs are turned OFF at the beginning of the program using function **sense.clear()**. Variables **oldx** and **oldy** are used to store the previous positions of the LED which was ON. The previous LED is turned OFF as the new LED is turned ON by the movement of the joystick.

```
#------------------------------------------------------------
#                    JOYSTICK LED CONTROL
#                    --------------------
#
# In this project the Sense HAT is connected to the
```

```
# Raspberry Pi 3. At the start of the program the LED
# at coordinates (0,0) is turned ON. Then the LEDs are
# turned ON by moving the joystick left, right, top,
# and bottom positions. In this program an LED that is
# turned On stays ON and therefore a pattern can be drawn
# by the LEDs using the joystick. The colour of the LEDs
# are chosen red in this program.
#
# In this modified program only one LED is ON at any time
#
# Author: Dogan Ibrahim
# File   : joystick2.py
# Date   : November, 2017
#-----------------------------------------------------------
import time
from sense_hat import SenseHat
sense = SenseHat()


#
# Turn ON the LED at (0,0) to start with. The LED at
# coordinates oldx and oldy (i.e. the previous LED ON
# coordinates) is turned OFF. All the LEDs are turned
# OFF at the beginning of the program
#
x = 0
y = 0
oldx = 0
oldy = 0
sense.clear()


#
# Start of main program loop. Check the joystick events
# and then turn the LEDs ON appropriately
#
while True:
    sense.set_pixel(oldx, oldy, [0,0,0])
    sense.set_pixel(x, y, [255,0,0])
    oldx = x
    oldy = y
    for event in sense.stick.get_events():
        if event.action == 'pressed' and event.direction == 'up':
            if y > 0:
                y = y - 1
        if event.action == 'pressed' and event.direction == 'down':
            if y < 7:
                y = y + 1
```

```
        if event.action == 'pressed' and event.direction == 'right':
          if x < 7:
            x = x + 1
        if event.action == 'pressed' and event.direction == 'left':
          if x > 0:
            x = x - 1
      time.sleep(0.5)
```

Figure 11.11 Modified program listing

The program given in Figure 11.11 can be further modified such that pressing the joystick turns OFF all the LEDs, i.e. clears the screen and turns ON the LED at the starting coordinate (0,0). The new program (joystick3.py) is shown in Figure 11.12.

```
#------------------------------------------------------------
#                    JOYSTICK LED CONTROL
#                    --------------------
#
# In this project the Sense HAT is connected to the
# Raspberry Pi 3. At the start of the program the LED
# at coordinates (0,0) is turned ON. Then the LEDs are
# turned ON by moving the joystick left, right, top,
# and bottom positions. In this program an LED that is
# turned On stays ON and therefore a pattern can be drawn
# by the LEDs using the joystick. The colour of the LEDs
# are chosen red in this program.
#
# In this modified program only one LED is ON at any time
# and also pressing the joystick clears the screen and turns
# ON the LED at coordinate (0,0)
#
# Author: Dogan Ibrahim
# File   : joystick3.py
# Date   : November, 2017
#------------------------------------------------------------
import time
from sense_hat import SenseHat
sense = SenseHat()

#
# Turn ON the LED at (0,0) to start with. The LED at
# coordinates oldx and oldy (i.e. the previous LED ON
# coordinates) is turned OFF. All the LEDs are turned
# OFF at the beginning of the program
#
x = 0
```

```
    y = 0
    oldx = 0
    oldy = 0
    sense.clear()

    #
    # Start of main program loop. Check the joystick events
    # and then turn the LEDs ON appropriately
    #
    while True:
      sense.set_pixel(oldx, oldy, [0,0,0])
      sense.set_pixel(x, y, [255,0,0])
      oldx = x
      oldy = y
      for event in sense.stick.get_events():
        if event.action == 'pressed' and event.direction == 'up':
          if y > 0:
            y = y - 1
        if event.action == 'pressed' and event.direction == 'down':
          if y < 7:
            y = y + 1
        if event.action == 'pressed' and event.direction == 'right':
          if x < 7:
            x = x + 1
        if event.action == 'pressed' and event.direction == 'left':
          if x > 0:
            x = x - 1
        if event.action == 'pressed' and event.direction == 'middle':
          sense.clear()
          oldx = 0
          oldy = 0
          x = 0
          y = 0
      time.sleep(0.5)
```

Figure 11.12 Modified program listing to clear the screen

11.11 PROJECT 2 – Display of Temperature by LED Count

Description: We have seen earlier in this Chapter how to read and display the environment variables on the LED matrix in the form of scrolling text. In this project we will be displaying the temperature in real-time by turning the correct number of LEDs ON. The display is refreshed every 2 seconds.

There are 64 LEDs in the LED matrix. For simplicity, we will assign each LED to 0.5ºC so that the temperature can be displayed from 0ºC (corresponding to no LEDs ON) to up to 32ºC (corresponding to all the 64 LEDs ON). If the temperature is less than 20º C the LEDs that are ON will be in RED colour. If on the other hand the temperature is higher, then the LEDs that are ON will be in GREEN colour.

Aim: The aim of this project is to show how the Sense HAT board can be used to read the ambient temperature and also how to display the temperature by \turning ON the correct number of LEDs.

Raspberry Pi Type: This project will run on all types of Raspberry Pi with 40-pin GPIO connector.

Block Diagram: Figure 11.13 shows the block diagram of the project.

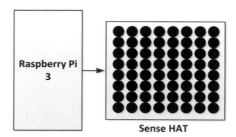

Figure 11.13 Block diagram of the project

Circuit Diagram: Sense HAT board is simply plugged-in on top of the Raspberry Pi 3.

Program: Figure 11.14 shows the program listing (program: sensetemp.py). At the beginning of the program modules time and sense_hat are imported to the program, and colours red, green, and no colour are defined. The LED matrix is then cleared just before entering the program loop. Inside the program loop the temperature is read and rounded to one decimal place. Variables **OnCount** and **OffCount** are set to the number of LEDs that should be ON and OFF respectively. Each ON LED is configured to correspond to 0.5 degrees Centigrade. Therefore, for example, if 20 LEDs are turned ON then the temperature is 10 degrees Centigrade. If the temperature is less than 20 degrees Centigrade then the number of red LEDs that should be ON are calculated. Similarly, if the temperature is not less than 20 degrees than the number of green LEDs that should be turned ON are calculated. The program displays the temperature by turning ON/OFF the LEDs. The program loop is repeated every 2 seconds.

```
#-----------------------------------------------------------------
#                    LED TEMPERTURE DISPLAY
#                    ----------------------
#
# In this project the Sense HAT is connected to the
# Raspberry Pi 3. The program reads the ambient temperature
# and displays it on the LED matrix where each LED turned ON
# corresponds to 0.5 degrees. Therefore, the temperature can
# be displayed from 0 degees to up to 32 degrees Centigrade
```

```
# by counting the number of LEDs that are turned ON. The
# display is updated every 2 seconds. If the temperature is
# less than 20 degrees Centigrade than the LEDs are red colour,
# otherwise they are green colour.
#
# Author: Dogan Ibrahim
# File   : sensetemp.py
# Date   : December, 2017
#-----------------------------------------------------------
import time
from sense_hat import SenseHat
sense = SenseHat()

#
# Define red (RED_ON), green (GREEN_ON) and no colours (OFF)
#
RED_ON = [255,0,0]
GREEN_ON = [0,255,0]
OFF = [0,0,0]

#
# Start of main program loop. Clear the LEDs just before
# entering the loop.Read the ambient temperature, round to
# one decimal place. If the temperature is less than 20
# degrees Centigrade then calculate teh number of red LEDs
# to be turned ON, otherwise calculate the number of green
# LEDs to be turned ON. Also, calculate the number of LEDs
# that should be OFF. Finally, display the temperature by
# turning the LEDs ON or OFF.
#
sense.clear()
while True:
  Temp = sense.get_temperature()      # read the temperature
  Temp = round(Temp , 1)              # round the reading
  leds = []                           # define a blank list
  OnCount = int(2*Temp)               # no of LEDs to be ON
  OffCount = 64 - OnCount             # no of LEDs to be OFF
  if Temp < 20:                       # if less than 20 degrees
    leds.extend([RED_ON]*OnCount)     # No of reds
  else:
    leds.extend([GREEN_ON]*OnCount)   # No of greens
  leds.extend([OFF]*OffCount)         # no of OFF
  sense.set_pixels(leds)              # turn ON/OFF LEDs
  time.sleep(2)                       # wait 2 seconds
```

Figure 11.14 Program listing

An example LED matrix displaying the temperature is shown in Figure 11.15. In this figure the measured temperature was 23 degrees Centigrade (46 LEDs are ON).

Figure 11.15 Temperature display (23 degrees Centigrade)

11.12 PROJECT 3 – Display of Temperature as LED Based Decimal Number
Description: In this project the ambient temperature is read in real-time and is displayed using the first three rows of the LED matrix. The temperature is displayed as two digit integer number where the LEDs on the first row display the first digit (10s) and the LEDs on the second and third rows display the second digit (1s). The LED at the (0, 0) coordinate is assumed to be number 0 of the first digit. Similarly, the LED at coordinate (0, 1) is assumed to be number 0 of the second digit. For example, 5ºC, 20 ºC, and 29ºC are displayed as shown in Figure 11.16. The temperature can be displayed from 0 ºC to up to 79 ºC.

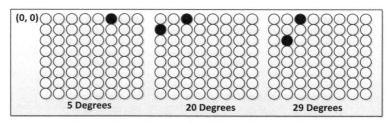

Figure 11.16 Displaying 5ºC, 20ºC and 29 ºC

The numbering of the digits are as follows:

First row:	0 1 2 3 4 5 6 7	(1's)
Second row:	0 1 2 3 4 5 6 7	(10's)
Third row:	8 9	(10's)

Aim: The aim of this project is to show how the Sense HAT board can be used to read the ambient temperature and also how to display the temperature by turning ON/OFF the LEDs on the first two rows of the LED matrix.

Raspberry Pi Type: This project will run on all types of Raspberry Pi with 40-pin GPIO connector.

Block Diagram: The block diagram of the project is as in Figure 11.13.

Circuit Diagram: Sense HAT board is simply plugged-in on top of the Raspberry Pi 3.

Program: Figure 11.17 shows the program listing (program: templed.py). At the beginning of the program modules time and sense_hat are imported to the program and colour red is defined. The reminder of the program is executed in an endless loop where the LED matrix is cleared and the temperature is read and the MSB and LSB digits are extracted and stored in variables **msb** and **lsb** respectively. If the LSB digit is greater than 7 then the third row of the display is used to display the 8 and 9 digits. The MSB digit is displayed on the first row of the LED matrix where the y coordinate is 0. The second digit is displayed on the second or the third row of the LED matrix depending on whether the digit is greater than 7 or not. The colour of the display is chosen to be red. The program loop is repeated every 2 seconds.

```
#----------------------------------------------------------------
#                      LED TEMPERTURE DISPLAY
#                      ---------------------
#
# In this project the Sense HAT is connected to the
# Raspberry Pi 3. The program reads the ambient temperature
# turning ON/OFF the LEDs in the first two rows of the LED
# matrix. In theory the temperature can be displayed in the
# range 0 to 798 degrees Centigrade. The LEDs are turned ON in
# red colour and the ddisplay is updated every 2 seconds.
# As an example, 27 degrees Centigrade is displayed as (here
# 0 corresponds to OFF LED and 1 corresponds to ON LED):
#
#    0 0 1 0 0 0 0 0
#    0 0 0 0 0 0 0 1
#    0 0 0 0 0 0 0 0
#    0 0 0 0 0 0 0 0
#    0 0 0 0 0 0 0 0
#    0 0 0 0 0 0 0 0
#    0 0 0 0 0 0 0 0
#    0 0 0 0 0 0 0 0
#
# Author: Dogan Ibrahim
# File   : templed.py
# Date   : December, 2017
#----------------------------------------------------------------
import time
from sense_hat import SenseHat
```

```
sense = SenseHat()

#
# Define red (RED_ON)
#
RED_ON = [255,0,0]


#
# Start of main program loop. Clear the LEDs at the beginning
# of the loop.Read the ambient temperature, round it to no
# decimal place, find the LEDs that has to be turned ON to
# display the temperature. First row of the LED matrix displays
# the MSB digit, while the second row displays the LSB digit.
# The program loop is repeated every 2 seconds.
#
while True:
    sense.clear()                       # clear LED matrix
    Temp = sense.get_temperature()      # read the temperature
    Temp = round(Temp , 0)              # round the reading
    msb = int(Temp / 10)                # get MSB digit
    lsb = int(Temp - 10*msb)            # get LSB digit
    y = 1                               # second row
    if lsb > 7:
        y = 2                           # third row
        lsb = lsb - 8
    x1 = msb                            # first row x coordinate
    x2 = lsb                            # second row x coordinate
    sense.set_pixel(x1, 0, [255,0,0]) # turn ON first row LED
    sense.set_pixel(x2, y, [255,0,0]) # turn ON second row LED
    time.sleep(2)                       # wait 2 seconds)
```

Figure 11.17 Program listing

A typical display is shown in Figure 11.18 where the measured temperature was 25 ºC.

Figure 11.18 Displaying the temperature on the LED matrix

11.13 PROJECT 4 – Sense HAT Flashing LED Christmas Lights

Description: In this project the 64 LEDs on the Sense HAT board are flashed randomly with random colours. The net effect is that a nice flashing display is obtained.

Aim: The aim of this project is to show how the random function can be used to flash all the LEDs on the Sense HAT board to create a nice visual display.

Raspberry Pi Type: This project will run on all types of Raspberry Pi with 40-pin GPIO connector.

Block Diagram: The block diagram of the project is as in Figure 11.13.

Circuit Diagram: Sense HAT board is simply plugged-in on top of the Raspberry Pi 3.

Program: Figure 11.19 shows the program listing (program: funled.py). At the beginning of the program modules time, random, and sense_hat are imported to the program. The program is executed in an endless loop where the random functions are used to generate random colours. In addition, the coordinates of the LEDs to be turned ON are generated randomly between 0 and 7. The program uses function sense.set_pixel to turn ON the selected LED with the selected colour. The LED matrix is cleared after all the LEDs (64) are turned ON.

```
#---------------------------------------------------------------
#                 FLASHING LED CHRISTMAS LIGHTS
#                 ---------------------------
#
# In this project the Sense HAT is connected to the
```

```
# Raspberry Pi 3. The program flashes all the LEDs on the LED
# matrix randomly with random colours. The LED to be turned
# ON and its colour are chosen randomly. All the possible
# colours are used in the program.
#
# Author: Dogan Ibrahim
# File   : funled.py
# Date   : December, 2017
#---------------------------------------------------------------
import time
import random
from sense_hat import SenseHat
sense = SenseHat()


#
# Start of main program loop. Clear the LEDs at the beginning
# of the loop. Generate random colours for the red, green and
# blue. Also generate the LED coordinates randomly between 0
# and 7. The net effect is that the LEDs make a pleasing
# flashing display that can be mounted on your Christmas tree.
# The display is refreshed after all the LEDs (64) are turned ON.
#
sense.clear()
i = 0
while True:
    r = random.randint(0, 255)
    g = random.randint(0, 255)
    b = random.randint(0, 255)
    x = random.randint(0, 7)
    y = random.randint(0, 7)
    sense.set_pixel(x, y, [r,g,b])
    time.sleep(0.01)
    i = i + 1
    if i == 64:
        i = 0
        sense.clear()
```

Figure 11.19 Program listing

11.14 PROJECT 5 – TALKING WEATHER FORECAST

Description: In this project a pair of speakers is connected to the Raspberry Pi in addition to the Sense HAT board and the environmental variables temperature, humidity, and pressure are read and sounded as speech on the speakers.

Aim: The aim of this project is to show how the eSpeak Python library can be used to convert text to speech and then send to speakers.

Raspberry Pi Type: This project will run on all types of Raspberry Pi with 40-pin GPIO connector and with at least one USB port and 3.5mm audio jack output.

Block Diagram: The block diagram of the project is as in Figure 11.20.

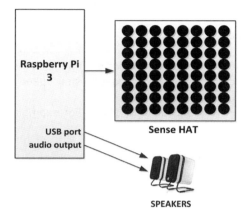

Figure 11.20 Block diagram of the project

Circuit Diagram: Sense HAT board is simply plugged-in on top of the Raspberry Pi 3. Any type of USB powered speaker can be used with this project. The speakers are powered from the USB port and are therefore should be connected to one of the USB ports of the Raspberry Pi. The 3.5mm audio plug of the speakers must be connected to audio input of the Raspberry Pi.

Program: The espeak module must be installed into your Raspberry Pi before it can be used. The command to install this library is:

pi@raspberrypi:~ $ **sudo apt-get install espeak python-espeak**

The features of espeak are:

- Includes different voices.
- Can produce speech output as a WAV file.
- It has compact size (around 2Mbytes)
- Supports HTML and SSML
- It can translate text into phoneme codes
- Supports many other languages
- Development tools are available

The espeak module includes many options. Some of the useful options are given below:

synth("text"): this command speaks the given text message

-v<voice filename> speaks in the specified language. For example, -ven speaks in

English, -vfr speaks in French, -ves speaks in Spanish and so on.

+m1 to +m5 speaks in different male voices

+f1 to +f4 speaks in different female voices

+whisper speaks as whispering

-s changes the speed of reading in words per minute. The default value is 175wpm. For example, the command −s90 changes to slow speed of 90 wpm

-g pauses between words in units of 10ms. For example, the command −g10 inserts 100 ms pause between words

Figure 11.21 shows the program listing (program: weather.py). At the beginning of the program, modules time, random, espeak, and sense_hat are imported to the program. The following functions have been created:

Speak_Date: tells the current date
Speak_Time: tells the current time
Speak_Temperature: tells the ambient temperature in degrees Celcius
Speak_Humidity: tells the ambient humidity as a percentage
Speak_Pressure: tells the atmospheric pressure in millibars

The program repeats every 10 seconds. Figure 11.22 shows the project assembly.

```
#------------------------------------------------------------
#                      TALKING WEATHER FORECAST
#                      -----------------------
#
# In this project the Sense HAT is connected to the
# Raspberry Pi 3. In addition a pair of speakers is
# connected to USB port and the 3.5mm audio input of
# the Raspberry Pi. The program reads the ambient
# temperature, humidity, and pressure and sends these
# readings to the speakers to tell the weather forecast
#
# Author: Dogan Ibrahim
# File   : weather.py
# Date   : December, 2017
#------------------------------------------------------------
from espeak import espeak
from datetime import datetime
import time
from sense_hat import SenseHat
sense = SenseHat()
```

```
#
# Get and then speak the current date
#
def Speak_Date():
  d = datetime.now().strftime("%d %m %G")
  espeak.synth("The date is %s" %d)
  time.sleep(5)


#
# Get and then speak the current time
#
def Speak_Time():
  t = datetime.now().strftime("%k %M")
  espeak.synth("The time is %s" %t)
  time.sleep(5)


#
# get and then speak the current temperature
#
def Speak_Temperature():
  T = sense.get_temperature()
  T = round(T, 1)
  espeak.synth("The temperature is %s degrees Celcius" %T)
  time.sleep(5)


#
# get and then speak the current humidity
#
def Speak_Humidity():
  H = sense.get_humidity()
  H = round(H, 1)
  espeak.synth("The humidity is %s Percent" %H)
  time.sleep(5)


#
# get and then speak the current pressure
#
def Speak_Pressure():
  P = sense.get_pressure()
  P = round(P, 1)
  espeak.synth("The barometric pressure is %s millibars" %P)
  time.sleep(5)


#
# Start of main program loop. Tell the heading, date and time
```

```
# and also the current ambient weather forecast
#
while True:
  espeak.synth("Weather forecast for today")
  time.sleep(2)
  Speak_Date()
  Speak_Time()
  Speak_Temperature()
  Speak_Humidity()
  Speak_Pressure()
  time.sleep(10)
```

Figure 11.21 Program listing

Figure 11.22 The project assembly

11.15 Summary

In this Chapter we have seen how to use the Sense HAT board to develop several interesting projects with the sensors on the board. In the next Chapter we shall be designing projects using a camera.

CHAPTER 12 • USING THE RASPBERRY PI CAMERA

12.1 Overview
In this Chapter we shall see how to use a camera with our Raspberry Pi 3. Programs codes and projects will be given to show how the camera can be used. There is also an infrared version of the camera, called Pi NoIR, which does not use an infrared filter and can be used in the dark with infrared lighting.

12.2 Features of the Raspberry Pi Camera
The Raspberry Pi camera (V2) is a fixed focus lens 8 megapixel camera using the IMX219 sensor from Sony, measuring just 25mm x 23mm x 9mm. The camera can take 3280 x 2464 pixel static images as well asc1080p30, 720p60, or 640x480p90 video. The camera is attached to the Raspberry Pi via a short ribbon cable through a small socket (CSI interface) on the board. Figure 12.1 shows the camera attached to the Raspberry Pi 3 board.

Figure 12.1 Attaching the camera to Raspberry Pi 3

12.3 Using the Camera
Connect your camera to the Raspberry Pi 3 as shown in Figure 12.1. Before using the camera make sure that your software is up to date. You can use the following commands to update your software:

        pi@raspberrypi:~ $ **sudo apt-get update**
        pi@raspberrypi:~ $ **sudo apt-get upgrade**

Enable the camera interface by the following steps:

- Enter command:

    pi@raspberrypi:~ **sudo raspi-config**

- Move the cursor down to select **Interface Options**

- Press Enter on option **Camera** to enable/disable the camera connection

- Select to enable the camera

- Select Finish to finish and return to the command mode

You can check whether or not the camera is working by taking a picture using the following command in the Raspberry Pi command mode. This command will start the camera to take a picture and store it in file called **camtest.jpeg** in the default user directory of **/home/ pi**. Command **raspistill** is used to capture still photographs with the camera. The filename must be specified after option –o. Options –vf and –hf can be attached to the command to flip the picture vertical or horizontal respectively. After taking the picture you can start the GUI desktop and select **Accessories ->Image Viewer** to view the image captured:

    pi@raspberrypi:~ $ **raspistill –o camtest.jpeg**

12.4 Using the Camera in Python Programs

Using the camera in Python programs is easy. Function **start_preview** is used to preview an image. Function **capture** is then used to capture an image where the name of the file where the image is to be installed must be supplied as an argument to this function. Function **stop_preview** stops the preview. Notice that the **start_preview** only works if the monitor is connected to the raspberry Pi. It will not work in the command mode or in the remote access (SSH) mode of access.

In the code given below, images are captured by the camera every 5 seconds and stored on the GUI Desktop in file myfile.jpg. You can double click on the image in Desktop to display its contents. Notice that it is necessary to give at least 2 seconds to the camera to adjust its sensor light levels:

```
import picamera
import time
with picamera.PiCamera() as camera:
        camera.start_preview()
        time.sleep(5)
        camera.capture("/home/pi/Desktop/myfile.jpg")
        camera.stop_preview()
```

Alternatively, we can write the above code as follows:

```
from picamera import PiCamera
import time
camera = PiCamera()
camera.start_preview()
time.sleep(5)
camera.capture("/home/pi/Desktop/myfile.jpg")
camera.stop_preview()
```

12.5 PROJECT 1 – CAPTURING MULTIPLE PICTURES

Description: In this project we will capture 5 different pictures with time intervals of 10 seconds and store all the four pictures in the Desktop. The pictures will be named MyPic0. jpg, MyPic1.jpg, MyPic2.jpg, MyPic3.jpg and MyPic4.jpg.

Aim: The aim of this project is to show how multiple pictures can be captured and stored on the desktop.

Raspberry Pi Type: This project will run on all types of Raspberry Pi.

Program: Figure 12.2 shows the program listing (program: multipic.py). At the beginning of the program modules time and picamera are added to the program. A loop is then formed where variable **c** takes the values 0,1,2,3, and 4. Five pictures are captured and stored on the desktop with 10 seconds between each picture.

```
#----------------------------------------------------------------
#
#            CAPTURING MULTIPLE PICTURES
#            ============================
#
# In this program 5 pictures are captured with 10 seconds
# intervals and these pictures are stored on the Desktop
# with the names Mypic0.jpg, MyPic1.jpg, MyPic2.jpg,
# MyPic3.jpg, MyPic4.jpg.
#
# Author: Dogan Ibrahim
# File   : multipic.py
# Date   : December, 2017
#----------------------------------------------------------------
import time
from picamera import PiCamera
camera = PiCamera()

camera.start_preview()

for c in range(5):
  time.sleep(5)
```

```
        camera.capture('/home/pi/Desktop/MyPic%s.jpg' % c)
    camera.stop_preview()
```

Figure 12.2 Program listing

12.6 Camera Settings
It is possible to change some camera settings in software. Some examples are given in this section.

12.6.1 Adding Text On Images
We can easily add text on images using the **annotate_text** keyword. An example code is given below where the text **My Picture** is added to the top of the image as shown in Figure 12.3:

```
from picamera import PiCamera
import time
camera = PiCamera()
camera.start_preview()
time.sleep(5)
camera.annotate_text = "My Picture"
camera.capture("/home/pi/Desktop/myfile.jpg")
camera.stop_preview()
```

Figure 12.3 Adding text on an image

The text size can be changed from 6 to 160 using the statement **camera.annotate_ text_size**, where the default setting is 32. By default, the text colour is white but it can be changed with the statement **camera.annotate_background** and **camera.annotate_ foreground**. In the following code the text background colour is set to white and the fore-ground colour is set to red:

```
from picamera import PiCamera, Color
import time
camera = PiCamera()
camera.start_preview()
```

```
time.sleep(5)
camera.annotate_background = Color('white')
camera.annotate_foreground = Color('red')
camera.annotate_text = "My Picture"
camera.capture("/home/pi/Desktop/myfile.jpg")
camera.stop_preview()
```

12.6.2 Changing the Brightness and Contrast of Images

The brightness and the contrast of an image can be changed using the statements: **camera.brightness** and **camera.contrast**. Valid values are from 0 to 100, with 50 being the default value. In the example code below the image brightness and contrast are increased before capturing the image:

```
from picamera import PiCamera
import time
camera = PiCamera()
camera.start_preview()
time.sleep(5)
camera.brightness = 80
camera.contrast = 70
camera.capture("/home/pi/Desktop/myfile.jpg")
camera.stop_preview()
```

12.6.3 Image Effects

The following image effects can be applied to an image using the statement **camera. image_effect** (the defaults is none):

none, negative, solarize, sketch, denoise, emboss, oilpaint, hatch, gpen, pastel, watercolor, film, blur, saturation, colorswap, washedout, posterise, colorpoint, colorbalance, cartoon, deinterlace1, and deinterlace2.

An example is shown below:

```
camera.image_effect = 'emboss'
```

12.6.4 Camera Exposure Image Modes

The following camera exposure modes can be applied to an image using the statement **camera.exposure_mode** (the defaults is auto):

off, auto, night, nightpreview, backlight, spotlight, sports, snow, beach, verylong, fixedfps, antishake, and fireworks.

An example is shown below:

```
camera.exposure_mode = 'snow'
```

12.7 Recording Video

Video recording is an easy task. You should replace **capture** with **start_recording** and **stop_recording**. An example code is given below which records for 10 seconds and then stops. You can play the recorded video using for example the raspberry Pi **omxplayer** software:

```
from picamera import PiCamera
import time
camera = PiCamera()
camera.start_preview()
camera.start_recording("/home/pi/myvideo.h264")
time.sleep(10)
camera.stop_recording()
camera.stop_preview()
```

12.8 PROJECT 2 – CAPTURING PICTURES USING A BUTTON

Description: In this project we will capture a picture every time a button is pressed, just like the shutter button of a camera. The captured pictures will be stored in the default user directory with the names MyPicn.jpeg where n is an integer number starting from 0.

Aim: The aim of this project is to show how pictures cab be captured after pressing a button.

Raspberry Pi Type: This project will run on all types of Raspberry Pi.

Block Diagram: The block diagram of the project is shown in Figure 12.4.

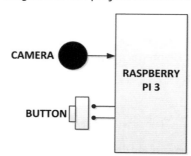

Figure 12.4 Block diagram of the project

Circuit Diagram: The circuit diagram of the project is shown in Figure 12.5 A button is connected between GPIO pin 2 and GND. The button state is normally at logic 1 and goes to logic 0 when the button is pressed.

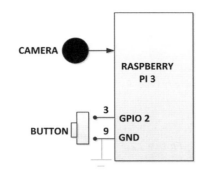

Figure 12.5 Circuit diagram of the project

Program: Figure 12.6 shows the program listing (program: cambutton.py). At the beginning of the program modules time, gpiozero, picamera are added to the program. A loop is then formed where variable **n** is initially set to 0 and is incremented by 1 every time the button is pressed. These numbers are used as part of the picture file names stored by the program. The file names are in the form MyPics**n**.jpg where **n** is the incrementing number. Function **button.wait_for_press** waits until the button is pressed. The program can be terminated by pressing the Cntrl+Z keys.

```
#-------------------------------------------------------------------
#
#                 CAPTURING PICTURES USING A BUTTON
#                 ================================
#
# In this program the camera is connected to the Raspberry Pi.
# In addition, a button is connected to GPIO 2. A picture is
# captured when the button is pressed. The captured pictures
# are stored in the default user directory with unique names
# of MyPicn.jpg where n is a number.
#
# The program terminates unorderly when Cntrl+Z is pressed.
#
# Author: Dogan Ibrahim
# File   : cambutton.py
# Date   : December, 2017
#-------------------------------------------------------------------
from picamera import PiCamera
from gpiozero import Button
camera = PiCamera()
button = Button(2)

camera.start_preview()
n = 0
#
# Start of the program loop. Check if the button is pressed
```

```
# and if so capture a picture and save it in file MyPicn.jpg
#
while True:
  button.wait_for_press()
  camera.capture('/home/pi/Desktop/MyPic%s.jpg' %n)
  n = n + 1
camera.stop_preview()
```

Figure 12.6 Program listing

Modified Program

The program given in Figure 12.6 is terminated unorderly by entering the Cntrl+Z keys. We can terminate the program orderly by pressing the Cntrl+C key on the keyboard. The modified program listing (program: cambutton1.py) is shown in Figure 12.7. Here, the keyboard interrupt routine is called as an exception when the Cntrl+C key is pressed. The camera is then stopped and the program is terminated.

```
#----------------------------------------------------------------
#
#                  CAPTURING PICTURES USING A BUTTON
#                  =================================
#
# In this program the camera is connected to the Raspberry Pi.
# In addition, a button is connected to GPIO 2. A picture is
# captured when the button is pressed. The captured pictures
# are stored in the default user directory with unique names
# of MyPicn.jpg where n is a number.
#
# In this version, pressing the Cntrl+C key on the keyboard
# terminates the program orderly.
#
# Author: Dogan Ibrahim
# File   : cambutton1.py
# Date   : December, 2017
#----------------------------------------------------------------
import sys
from picamera import PiCamera
from gpiozero import Button
camera = PiCamera()
button = Button(2)

camera.start_preview()
n = 0

#
# Start of the program loop. Check if the button is pressed
```

```
# and if so capture and save a picture in file MyPicn.jpg
#
while True:
  try:
    button.wait_for_press()
    camera.capture('/home/pi/Desktop/MyPic%s.jpg' %n)
    n = n + 1
  except KeyboardInterrupt:
    camera.stop_preview()
    sys.exit()
```

Figure 12.7 Modified program listing

12.9 PROJECT 3 – RECORDING VIDEO USING A BUTTON

Description: In this project we will start and stop video recording using a button.

Aim: The aim of this project is to show how video recording can be started and stopped using a button.

Raspberry Pi Type: This project will run on all types of Raspberry Pi.

Block Diagram: The block diagram of the project is as in Figure 12.4.

Circuit Diagram: The circuit diagram of the project is as in Figure 12.5.

Program: Figure 12.8 shows the program listing (program: videobutton.py). At the beginning of the program modules time, gpiozero, picamera are added to the program. A loop is then formed where the program checks if the button is pressed and if so start video recording. The recording is stored in file **MyVideo.h264** in user's default directory of **/home/pi**. The recording stops when the button is pressed again. The program is terminated orderly when the Cntrl+C key is pressed.

```
#--------------------------------------------------------------
#
#              RECORDING VIDEO USING A BUTTON
#              ==============================
#
# In this program the camera is connected to the Raspberry Pi.
# In addition, a button is connected to GPIO 2. Video recording
# starts whne the button is pressed. The recording stops when
# the button is pressed again. Pressing the Cntrl+C key on the
# keyboard terminates the program orderly.
#
# Author: Dogan Ibrahim
# File  : videobutton.py
# Date  : December, 2017
```

```
#----------------------------------------------------------------
import sys
from picamera import PiCamera
from gpiozero import Button
camera = PiCamera()
button = Button(2)

camera.start_preview()

#
# Start of the program loop. Check if the button is pressed
# and if so start recording and save the recording in file
# MyVideo.h264
#
while True:
  try:
    button.wait_for_press()
    camera.start_recording('/home/pi/MyVideo.h264')
    n = n + 1
    time.sleep(2)
    button.wait_for_press()
    camera.stop_recording()
  except KeyboardInterrupt:
    camera.stop_preview()
    sys.exit()
```

Figure 12.8 Program listing

Figure 12.9 shows the button mounted on a breadboard and connected to the Raspberry Pi 3 using jumper wires.

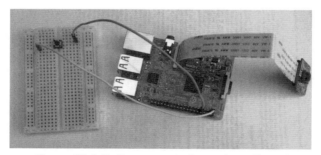

Figure 12.9 Button mounted on a breadboard

12.10 Summary

In this Chapter we have seen how to use the Raspberry Pi camera. The next Chapter is about controlling motors with the Raspberry Pi using the MotoPi board.

CHAPTER 13 • USING THE MotoPI Board

13.1 Overview
In this Chapter we shall see how to use the MotoPi motor control board with our Raspberry Pi 3. Programs codes and projects will be given to show how this board can be used to control servo motors.

13.2 Features of the MotoPi Board
The MotoPi is an extension board having 16 PWM channels that can be used to control up to 16 servo motors operating at 5V (5V DC input) with current consumptions up to 6A. The board can also be powered from external 4.8V and 6V (4.8-6V DC input) power supply with currents up to 6A so that larger motors can be connected to the board. The board is compatible with all models of Raspberry Pi with 40-pin GPIO socket and can be programmed using the Python interpreter.

The MotoPi board also has 4 analog, 2 digital, and one I2C interface ports. An on-board crystal oscillator provides accurate timing.

Figure 13.1 shows the MotoPi board where various parts of the board have been identified.

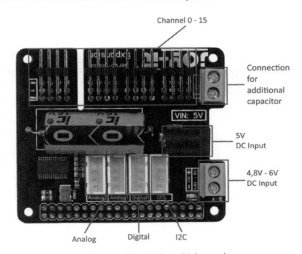

Figure 13.1 MotoPi board

The 16 channel numbers are written at the backside of the board as shown in Figure 13.2. Each channel has 3 pins: GND, V+, and PWM. A large capacitor on the board prevents sudden voltage drops. An additional capacitor can be connected in parallel with this capacitor if required through the 2-pin screw terminal located at the top right hand side of the board.

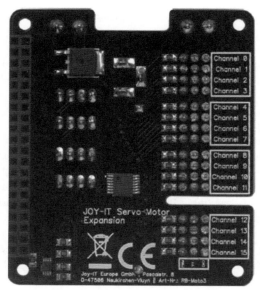

Figure 13.2 Channel numbers at the backside of the board

You should plug-in the MotoPi board on top of your Raspberry Pi. The MotoPi board communicates with the Raspberry Pi through the SPI bus. It is therefore necessary to enable the I2C bus interface on your Raspberry Pi using the **sudo raspi-config** command. You should select the **Interface Options** and then select to enable the **SPI** interface. Reboot your Raspberry Pi after enabling the SPI.

The Python library provided by the manufacturer of the MotoPi board is recommended to be used while accessing the board. This library can be installed as follows:
Click on the following link to download the library zip file (the library is a modified version of the Adafruit_PCA9685 library):

http://cloud.joy-it.net/index.php/s/1rdGoz3QNx8nYil

Extract the files and then copy the extracted files into a folder on your Raspberry Pi, and navigate to this folder (see Figure 13.3). You can use the WinSCP file copy program to copy the files from the PC to the Raspberry Pi. In this example, a folder called MotoPi has been created on the Raspberry Pi and the files are copied into this folder.

Name	Date modified	Type
setuptools-3.5.1.zip	30/11/2017 18:49	Compressed (zip
Adafruit_Python_PCA9685.zip	30/11/2017 18:49	Compressed (zip
ez_setup.py	30/11/2017 18:49	PY File
ez_setup.pyc	30/11/2017 18:49	Compiled Pytho
LICENSE	30/11/2017 18:49	File
README.md	30/11/2017 18:49	MD File
setup.py	30/11/2017 18:49	PY File
.gitignore	30/11/2017 18:49	Text Document
Adafruit_PCA9685	30/11/2017 18:49	File folder
Adafruit_PCA9685.egg-info	30/11/2017 18:49	File folder
build	30/11/2017 18:49	File folder
dist	30/11/2017 18:49	File folder
examples	30/11/2017 18:49	File folder
.git	30/11/2017 18:49	File folder

Figure 13.3 Files in folder motopi

Install the library by entering the following commands:

> pi@raspberrypi:~ $ **cd motopi**
> pi@raspberrypi:~ /motopi $ **sudo python setup.py install**

Enter the following commands to install the spidev and wiringpi, and then reboot your Raspberry Pi:

> pi@raspberrypi:~ /motopi $ **cd ..**
> pi@raspberrypi:~ $ **sudo apt-get update**
> pi@raspberrypi:~ $ **sudo pip install spidev**
> pi@raspberrypi:~ $ **sudo pip install wiringpi**
> pi@raspberrypi:~ $ **sudo reboot**

13.3 Analog and Digital Ports

Figure 13.4 shows the connection diagram of the 4 analog ports, named as A0, A1, A2 and A3. The connection diagram of the digital ports is shown in Figure 13.5. The I2C interface pins are shown in Figure 13.6.

Figure 13.4 Analog ports

Figure 13.5 Digital ports

Figure 13.6 I2C pins

13.3 PROJECT 1 - Using the Analog Ports

Description: In this project a TMP36 type analog temperature sensor chip is connected to one of the analog ports of the MotoPi board. The ambient temperature is read and displayed on the monitor every two seconds.

Aim: The aim of this project is to show how the analog input ports of the MotoPi ADC can be used in a Python program.

Raspberry Pi Type: This project will run on all types of Raspberry Pi with 40 pin GPIO connectors.

Block Diagram: The block diagram of the project is shown in Figure 13.7. The output of TMP36 temperature sensor chip is connected to channel A0 of the MotoPi board. The ADC on the MotoPi is the MCP3004 chip which is a quad ADC with 10 bits of resolution, having the reference voltage of 3.3V.

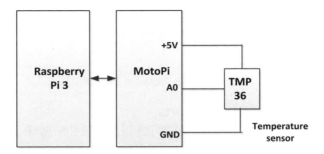

Figure 13.7 Block diagram of the project

Program: Figure 13.8 shows the program listing (program: anamotopi.py). Because the ADC is 10-bits wide, it has 1024 quantization levels, and the ADC reference voltage is 3.3V. At the beginning of the program modules time and spidev are imported to the program. A function called **readadc** is created to read the analog data. The program is executed in an endless loop. Inside this loop the temperature is read and converted into degrees Celsius and displayed on the monitor every 2 seconds.

```
#---------------------------------------------------------
#
#              READ ANALOG DATA FROM MotoPi
#
# In this project a TMP36 type analog temperature
# sensor is connected to analog port A0 of the MotoPi
# board. The program reads and displays the ambient
# temperature on the monitor every 2 seconds.
#
# Author: Dogan Ibrahim
# Date   : December, 2017
# File   : anamotopi.py
#---------------------------------------------------------
import spidev
import time

spi = spidev.SpiDev()
spi.open(0,0)

def readadc(adcnum):
    r = spi.xfer2([1,(8+adcnum) << 4, 0])
    adcout = ((r[1] & 3) << 8) + r[2]
    return adcout

while True:
    value = readadc(0)
    mv = value * 3300.0/1024.0
```

```
Temp = (mv - 500) / 10.0
print(Temp)
time.sleep(1)
```

Figure 13.8 Program listing

13.4 PROJECT 2 - Using the Digital Ports

Description: In this project an LED is connected to one of the digital ports of the MotoPi board and this LED is flashed every second.

Aim: The aim of this project is to show how the digital ports of the MotoPi board can be used in a Python program.

Raspberry Pi Type: This project will run on all types of Raspberry Pi with 40 pin GPIO connectors.

Block Diagram: The block diagram of the project is shown in Figure 13.9. The LED is connected to GPIO port 22 through a 390 ohm current limiting resistor.

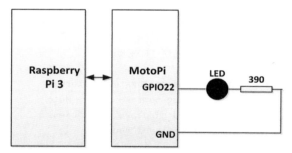

Figure 13.9 Block diagram of the project

Program: Figure 13.10 shows the program listing (program: digimotopi.py). At the beginning of the program modules time and RPi.GPIO are imported to the program and GPIO port 22 is configured as an output. The program is executed in an endless loop where inside this loop the LED is flashed every second. Figure 13.11 shows the LED mounted on a breadboard and connected to the MotoPi board using two jumper cables.

```
#-----------------------------------------------------------
#
#               FLASH AN LED CONNECTED TO MotoPi
#               =================================
#
# In this project an LEd is connected to port pin GPIO22
# of the MotoPi board. the program flashes teh LED every
# second
#
# Author: Dogan Ibrahim
```

```
# Date   : December, 2017
# File   : digimotopi.py
#-----------------------------------------------------
import RPi.GPIO as GPIO
import time

LED = 22
GPIO.setwarnings(False)
GPIO.setmode(GPIO.BCM)
GPIO.setup(LED, GPIO.OUT)

#
# Start of program loop to flash the LD every second
#
while True:
  GPIO.output(LED, 1)
  time.sleep(1)
  GPIO.output(LED, 0)
  time.sleep(1)
```

Figure 13.10 Program listing

Figure 13.11 LED on a breadboard

13.5 Servo Motors

Servo motors are DC motors, used in many position control applications where it is required to position the motor shaft at a desired position. These motors use built-in position sensing devices to determine the position of their shafts, and then rotate in the correct direction to position the motor shafts at the commanded positions. Servo motors do not rotate freely round and round like a normal motor, but rather they can turn around 180 degrees or so back and forth.

Unlike other motors, servo motors have 3 wire connections: power, ground, and control signal. The control signal is positive going Pulse Width Modulated (PWM) voltage such that the frequency of this voltage (or the period) is fixed, but the duration varies in relation to the required position of the motor shaft. For example, the popular TowerPro SG90 servo motor operates such that the period of the PWM signal is 20 ms (frequency of 50 Hz) so that the motor checks the duration of the pulse every 20 ms. The motor shaft is in the middle when the pulse duration is 1.5 ms, 90 degrees all the way to the right when the pulse duration is 2 ms, and -90 degrees all the way to the left when the pulse duration is 1 ms.

Figure 13.12 shows the SG90 servo motor together with its wiring diagram. This motor has the following features:

- Operating voltage: 3.3V to 6V
- Running current (at +5V): 220 ±50 mA
- Stall current (at +5V): 650 ±80 mA
- Idle current (at +5V): 6±10 mA
- Weight: 9 g
- Stall torque: 1.8 kgf.cm
- Speed: 0.1 s/60 degree

Signal input of the motor is the yellow wire, power supply input is the red wire, and the ground input is the brown wire.

Ground
+V, Power
Signal

Figure 13.12 SG90 servo motor

13.6 MotoPi PWM Channels

The 16 PWM channels each have 12-bits of resolution and they are based on the Adafruit PCA9685 Python library. The following functions are available in the library:

set_pwm_freq(freq): This function is used to set the PWM frequency between

40Hz and 1000Hz. Remember that the period of the PWM waveform is equal to the inverse of its frequency. i.e. T = 1 / f. As example, the following function call sets the PWM frequency to 100Hz:

set_pwm_freq(100)

set_pwm(channel, on, off): This function sets the start (on), and end (off) of the high segment of the PWM pulse on the specified channel. The channel number must be between 0 and 15 and the on/off values must be between 0 and 4095. **on** specifies when the PWM pulse should go from low-to-high, and **off** specifies when the pulse should go from high-to-low. As an example, assuming that the period of the PWM waveform is 20 ms, the following function call sets channel 1 to go low-to-high at 25% into the pulse (100 x 1024/4096 %, i.e. 5 ms), and back to low 75% into the pulse (100 x 3072/4096 %, i.e. 10 ms), and remain low for the last 25% (i.e. 5 ms) of the pulse. Figure 13.13 shows the generated PWM pulse for this example.

set_pwm(1, 1024, 3072)

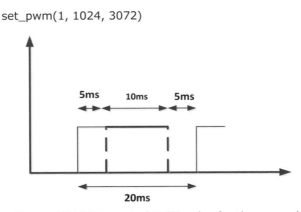

Figure 13.13 Generated PWM pulse for the example

Calculating the on/off tick numbers for the required pulse width
We can calculate the pulse width in microseconds as follows:

- Calculate the required PWM period in microseconds from T = 1 / f
- Divide by 4096 to get the time per tick
- Divide the required pulse width in microseconds to time per tick
- Turn **on** at 0, and turn **off** at the calculated tick number

Expressing the calculation mathematically, we can write:

OFF tick = 4096 x P / T
T = 1 / f
ON tick = 0

Where, P is the required pulse width in microseconds, T is the period in microseconds, OFF and ON ticks are the off and on tick numbers where the pulse should change from high-to-low and from low-to-high respectively.

As an example, assuming that channel 2 is to be used and the PWM frequency is 50Hz and the required pulse width is 1000 microseconds, we can calculate the OFF tick as follows:

> T = 1 / 50 = 20ms, or 20000 microseconds
> OFF tick = 4096 x 1000 / 20000 = 204
> ON tick = 0

Therefore, the required functions are:

> set_pwm_freq(50)
> set_pwm(2, 0, 204)

Calculating the on/off tick numbers for the required duty cycle

The duty cycle is defined as the percentage:

> Duty cycle = (Pulse width / period) x 100 %

or,   D = (P / T) x 100 %

Assuming that the ON tick time is set to 0, the relationship between the duty cycle and the OFF tick number can be calculated as follows:

> P = T x D / 100

Therefore, OFF tick = 4096 x P / T = 4096 x T x D /(100 x T)

or, OFF tick = 4096 x D / 100

or, finally, OFF tick = 40.96 x D

As an example, assuming the required duty cycle is, D = 5% (1 ms pulse width for 20 ms period), the OFF tick should be:

> OFF tick = 40.96 x 5 = 204

13.7 PROJECT 3 – Simple Servo Motor Control
Description: In this project a small servo motor is connected to one of the channels of the MotoPi board. The program swings the servo arm from left to right and then from right to left with a small delay between each movement. Each movement is set to be 10° and 0.1 second delay is inserted between each movement.

Aim: The aim of this project is to show how a small servo motor can be controlled using the MotoPi board.

Raspberry Pi Type: This project will run on all types of Raspberry Pi with 40 pin GPIO connectors.

Block Diagram: The block diagram of the project is shown in Figure 13.14. A small SG90 type servo motor is used in this project. The servo motor is connected to channel 1 of the MotoPi PWM port as shown in Figure 13.15. An external 5V DC power supply must be connected to the MotoPi 5V power input.

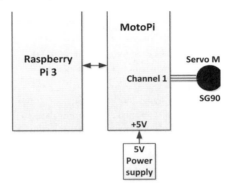

Figure 13.14 Block diagram of the project

Figure 13.15 Servo motor connected to channel 1

Program: Figure 13.16 shows the program listing (program: servopi1.py). At the beginning of the program, modules time and Adafruit_PCA9685 are imported to the program. The program runs in an endless loop where the arm of the servo motor is moved in 10° from left to right, and then from right to left with 0.1 second delay between each movement.

According to its specification, the SG90 servo motor arm is at the middle position when the pulse width is 1.5 ms, and at position 90º (the arm all the way to the right) when the pulse width is 2 ms, and at position -90º (all the way to the left) when the pulse width is 1 ms. Therefore, 90º movement of the motor arm corresponds to 0.5 ms change in the pulse width. i.e. 10º change in the arm position corresponds to 0.05 ms change in the pulse width. In the program, the pulse width starts from 1 ms and is incremented by 0.05 ms to 2 ms with 0.1 second delay between each change.

1 ms and 2 ms pulse widths correspond to OFF tick numbers of 204 and 410 respectively. Similarly, the increment 0.05 ms corresponds to OFF tick number of 10. Therefore, the OFF tick number is started from 200 and is incremented to 410 in steps of 10.

```
#-------------------------------------------------------------
#
#                  MotoPi SIMPLE SERVO MOTOR CONTROL
#                  ================================
#
# In this project an SG90 type servo motor is connected
# to channel 1 of the MotoPi board. The program swings
# the motor arm from left to right and then right to
# left with 0.1 second between each step where a step
# corresponds to 10 degrees.
#
# Author: Dogan Ibrahim
# Date   : December, 2017
# File   : servopi1.py
#-------------------------------------------------------------
import time
import Adafruit_PCA9685


pwm = Adafruit_PCA9685.PCA9685(address=0x41)


#
# Define the servo start and servo end numbers
#
channel = 1              # set channel 1
ServoStart = 100         # start OFF tick number
ServoEnd = 450           # end OFF tick number
ServoStep = 10           # step

pwm.set_pwm_freq(50)     # set PWM frequency to 50 Hz

while True:
    servo = ServoStart
    while (servo <= ServoEnd):
        pwm.set_pwm(channel, 0, servo)
        time.sleep(0.1)
```

```
        servo = servo + 10

    servo = ServoEnd
    while (servo >= ServoStart):
        pwm.set_pwm(channel, 0, servo)
        time.sleep(0.1)
        servo = servo - 10
```

Figure 13.16 Program listing

It was found by the author that in practise the servo motor did not behave exactly as specified in its data sheet. In practice, the OFF tick number was set to change from 100 to 450 for full swing of the servo motor arm, instead of from 204 to 410. Therefore, the motor you are using may need different settings for full swing.

13.8 PROJECT 4 – Servo Motor Controlled Obstacle Detection

Description: In this project an ultrasonic transmitter/receiver module is mounted on the SG90 servo motor arm. As the motor arm swings from right to left so does the ultrasonic module and the distances to the obstacles in front of the ultrasonic module are measured and displayed on the monitor in the form of a table where the angle and the distance to any obstacle are tabulated. One typical application of this project is that the servo motor and the ultrasonic transmitter/receiver module can be mounted on a mobile robot to detect and avoid any obstacles around the robot.

Aim: The aim of this project is to show how a servo motor controlled obstacle detection project can be developed using an ultrasonic transmitter/receiver module.

Raspberry Pi Type: This project will run on all types of Raspberry Pi with 40 pin GPIO connectors.

Block Diagram: The block diagram of the project is shown in Figure 13.17.

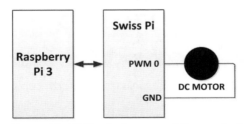

Figure 13.17 Block diagram of the project

Circuit Diagram: Figure 13.18 shows the circuit diagram of the project. The servo motor is connected to channel 1 of the MotoPi as shown in Figure 13.15. The ultrasonic transmitter/receiver **trig** and **echo** pins are connected to GPIO pins 22 and 27 on the MotoPi respectively. Remember to connect an external +5V power supply to power input of the MotoPi board.

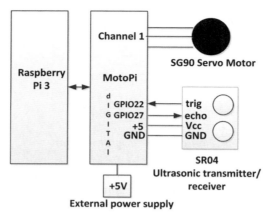

Figure 13.18 Circuit diagram of the project

The SR04 ultrasonic transmitter (see Figure 13.19) has the following specifications:

- Operating voltage (current): 5V (2 mA)
- Detection distance: 2 cm – 450 cm
- Input trigger signal 10 microseconds TTL
- Sensor angle: not more than 15 degrees
- The module has the following pins:
- Vcc: +V power input
- Trig: Trigger input
- Echo: Echo output
- Gnd: Power ground

Figure 13.19 SR04 ultrasonic transmitter/receiver module

The principle of operation of the ultrasonic sensor module is as follows:

- A 10us trigger pulse is sent to the module
- The module then sends eight 40kHz square wave signals and automatically detects the returned (echoed) pulse signal
- If an echo signal is returned the time to receive this signal is recorded

The distance to the object is calculated as:

Distance to object (in metres) = (time to received echo in seconds * speed of sound) / 2

The speed of sound is 340 m/s, or 34000 cm/s

Therefore,

Distance to object (in cm) = 34000 x time / 2

Where time is in seconds and it is the time taken to receive the echo pulse. We can re-write the above equation as:

Distance to object (in cm) = 17000 x time

Figure 13.20 shows the principle of operation of the ultrasonic sensor module. For example, if the time to receive the echo is 294 microseconds (0.000294 second) then the distance to the object is calculated as:

Distance to object (cm) = 0.000294 * 17000 = 5 cm

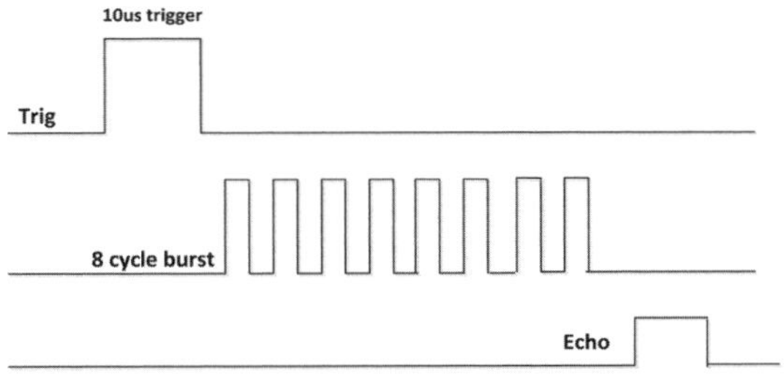

Figure 13.20 Operation of the ultrasonic sensor module

Program: Figure 13.21 shows the program listing (program: servopi2.py). At the beginning of the program, modules time and Adafruit_PCA9685 and RPi.GPIO are imported to the program and pins trigger and echo are assigned o GPIO ports 22 and 27 respectively. GPIO 22 is configured as output and GPIO 27 is configured as input. The frequency of the PWM waveform is set to 50 Hz.

Function **GetDistance** calculates the distance (in cm) to any obstacle by sending a trigger pulse and waiting for the echo pulse as described above. The time to the echo pulse is calculated in seconds. The program loop is executed every 10 seconds. Inside this loop the table header is displayed. The distance to any obstacles is calculated for the angles 0 to 180 degrees in steps of 10 degrees as the servo motor arm swings from right to left and is displayed in tabular form. 2 seconds of delay is inserted between each calculation. Notice that the servo arm swings from right to left where furthest right is considered to be angle 0 and furthest left is considered to be 180 degrees.

```
#--------------------------------------------------------------
#
#          SERVO MOTOR CONTROLLED OBSTACLE DETECTION
#          ==========================================
#
# In this project an SG90 type servo motor is connected
# to channel 1 of the MotoPi board. In addition, an SR04
# type ultrsonic transmitter/receiver module is connected
# to GPIO pins 22 and 27 of the MotoPi digital ports. The
# ultrasonic transmitter/receiver module is mounted on the
# servo motor arm so that as the servo arm swings so does
# the ultrasonic transmitter/receiver module. The program
# finds the distance to the obstacles in front of the sensor
# as the sensor mover 180 degrees from left to right in steps
# of 10 degrees. The angle and the distance to any obstacles
# at this angle position are tabulated on the monitor. The
# display is updated every 10 seconds.
#
# The trig ans the echo pins of the ultraonic transmitter/
# receiver module are connected to GPIO pins 22 and 27
# respectively.
#
# Author: Dogan Ibrahim
# Date   : December, 2017
# File   : servopi2.py
#--------------------------------------------------------------
#
# Import the required library modules
#
import RPi.GPIO as GPIO
import time
import Adafruit_PCA9685

pwm = Adafruit_PCA9685.PCA9685(address=0x41)
GPIO.setwarnings(False)
GPIO.setmode(GPIO.BCM)

#
# Ultrasonic transmitter/receiver pins
#
trig = 22                        # GPIO22
echo = 27                        # GPIO27

#
# Configure GPIO22 as output and GPIO27 as input
#
```

```
GPIO.setup(trig, GPIO.OUT)
GPIO.setup(echo, GPIO.IN)

#
# Define the servo start and servo end numbers
#
channel = 1                     # set channel 1
ServoStart = 100                # start OFF tick number
ServoEnd = 450                  # end OFF tick number
ServoStep = 10                  # step

pwm.set_pwm_freq(50)            # set PWM frequency to 50 Hz

#
# This function calculates the distance to any obstacles
# in centimetres
#
def GetDistance():
  GPIO.output(trig, 0)          # wait to settle
  time.sleep(0.08)
  GPIO.output(trig, 1)          # send trig
  time.sleep(0.00001)           # wait 10 microseconds
  GPIO.output(trig, 0)          # remove trig
  while GPIO.input(echo) == 0:  # wait until echo is received
    start_time = time.time()    # start time

  while GPIO.input(echo) == 1:  # echo received
    end_time = time.time()      # end time

  pulse_width = end_time - start_time
  distance = pulse_width * 17000
  return distance

#
# Display static heading on the monitor, and tabulate
# the angle and the distance to any obstacles. The angle
# is in degrees and the distance is in cm
#
while True:
  print("ANGLE    DISTANCE TO OBSTACLE")
  print("=====    ====================")
  servo = ServoStart
  Angle = 0
  while (Angle <= 180):
    pwm.set_pwm(channel, 0, servo)
    time.sleep(2)
```

```
    Obstacle = GetDistance()
    print("%3d            %d" %(Angle, Obstacle))
    servo = servo + 20
    Angle = Angle + 10
time.sleep(10)
print("")
```

Figure 13.21 Program listing

Figure13.22 shows a typical output displayed on the monitor as a table where the angle and the distance to any obstacles in that direction are tabulated.

```
pi@raspberrypi:~ $ python servopi2.py
ANGLE    DISTANCE TO OBSTACLE
=====    ====================
  0             75
 10            164
 20            165
 30            165
 40            165
 50             99
 60             96
 70             94
 80             95
 90             76
100             75
110             74
120             77
130             75
140             75
150             83
160            110
170            110
180            111
```

Figure 13.22 Typical output displayed on the monitor

Figure 13.23 shows the project assembly with the ultrasonic module mounted on the servo motor arm so that as the servo arm swings so does the ultrasonic arm.

Figure 13.23 Project assembly

13.9 Summary
In this Chapter the use of the MotoPi board has been shown with simple projects. In the next Chapter we shall be looking at using the Swiss Pi I/O board in Raspberry Pi projects.

CHAPTER 14 • USING THE Swiss Pi Board

14.1 Overview

In this Chapter we shall see how to use the Swiss Pi I/O card can be used with our Raspberry Pi 3. Programs codes and projects will be given to show how this card can be used in various simple projects.

14.2 Features of the Swiss Pi Card

The Swiss Pi card (see Figure 14.1) has the following basic features:

- 16 GPIO channels with individually configurable direction and pull-up resistors
- 16 PWM channels each 12-bits, operating 40 to 1000 Hz
- 4 servo motor connections, 10 mA source, 25 mA sink current at 5V
- 8 channel 12-bit ADC with internal reference and clock
- Half-duplex RS-485 interface
- Battery (type: CR2032) backed real-time clock and calendar with integrated oscillator and 32.768 kHz crystal
- I2C bus extension connector
- Polyfuse on 5V line to protect damage to the computer
- Slot for camera cable
- Cutout for display cable
- Incorporates EEPROM

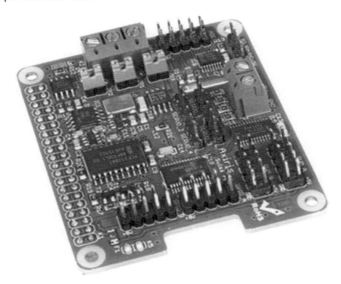

Figure 14.1 The Swiss Pi I/O card

Further information on Swiss Pi and the **Swiss Pi User Manual** are available at the following link:

https://www.axiris.eu/en/index.php/i-o-cards/swiss-pi

Figure 14.2 shows the Swiss Pi card block diagram. There are 2 x I2C busses and an SPI bus on-board. The SPI bus is dedicated to the RS-485 interface. The I2C bus supports maximum 400 kHz bus speeds. The addresses of the two I2C busses are:

I2C1

Address	Device	Description
1010001b	PCF2129A	RTC
0100000b	MCP23017	GPIO
0110011b	MAX11614	ADC
1001000b	PCA9685	PWM

I2C2

Address	Device	Description
1010000b	24C32	EEPROM

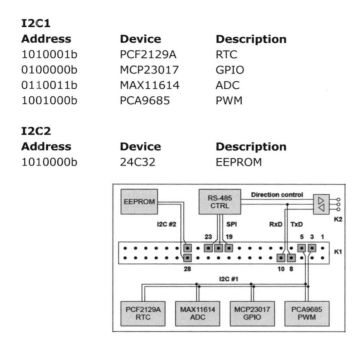

Figure 14.2 Block diagram of the Swiss Pi card

Figure 14.3 shows the description of the components on the Swiss Pi card. The pin configurations of the various components on the board are shown in Figure 14.4.

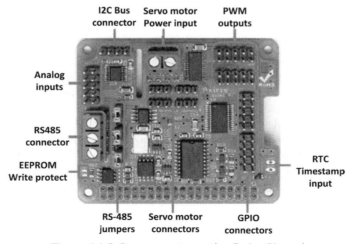

Figure 14.3 Components on the Swiss Pi card

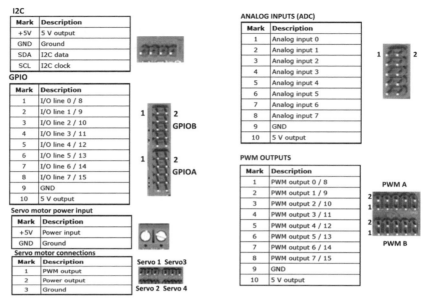

I2C

Mark	Description
+5V	5 V output
GND	Ground
SDA	I2C data
SCL	I2C clock

GPIO

Mark	Description
1	I/O line 0 / 8
2	I/O line 1 / 9
3	I/O line 2 / 10
4	I/O line 3 / 11
5	I/O line 4 / 12
6	I/O line 5 / 13
7	I/O line 6 / 14
8	I/O line 7 / 15
9	GND
10	5 V output

Servo motor power input

Mark	Description
+5V	Power input
GND	Ground

Servo motor connections

Mark	Description
1	PWM output
2	Power output
3	Ground

ANALOG INPUTS (ADC)

Mark	Description
1	Analog input 0
2	Analog input 1
3	Analog input 2
4	Analog input 3
5	Analog input 4
6	Analog input 5
7	Analog input 6
8	Analog input 7
9	GND
10	5 V output

PWM OUTPUTS

Mark	Description
1	PWM output 0 / 8
2	PWM output 1 / 9
3	PWM output 2 / 10
4	PWM output 3 / 11
5	PWM output 4 / 12
6	PWM output 5 / 13
7	PWM output 6 / 14
8	PWM output 7 / 15
9	GND
10	5 V output

Figure 14.4 Pin configurations

The board features sixteen general-purpose I/O lines numbered 0 to 15. Lines 0 to 7 are available on connector GPIO A, lines 8 to 15 are available on connector GPIO B.

The I/O lines operate at 5 V. Each I/O line can be configured as input or output, and features a pull-up resistor.

The board features sixteen PWM output lines numbered 0 to 15. Lines 0 to 7 are available on connector PWM A, lines 8 to 15 are available on connector PWM B.The PWM lines operate at 5 V level. They are particularly suitable for driving LEDs and servo motors. PWM outputs 0 to 3 are also routed to connectors SERVO [1..4].

14.3 The Software

The Swiss Server software uses network ports and communications protocols to provide functions to the Swiss Pi. The server can accept multiple client connections, thus allowing seceral clients to work with the Swiss Pi concurrently. A client sends a command, and the server returns a response after the command is executed. The communication protocol is in standard ASCII format. The server supports a large number of commands for working with the Swiss Pi card. The communication protocol is fully asynchronous, meaning that the client does not have to wait for the response to a command before sending the next command. As a result, the clients can send several commands in succession, therefore increasing the communication efficiency. The server also has an option for exchanging data bytes directly between the RS-485 interface and a network port. If this option is disabled, clients can use commands to send data bytes over the RS-485 interface.

Before using the Swiss Pi we have to start the Swiss Server program on our Raspberry Pi 3. The steps for this are given below:

- Plug-in the Swiss Pi card on top of your Raspberry Pi board

- Go to the Axiris Software Repository web page using your PC:

    https://www.axiris.eu/en/index.php/free-software/software-repository

- Click on the following link to download the Swiss Server program:

    public-2016-11-06-linux-armhf.tar.gz

Copy all the programs to a folder on your PC. In the example below, all the files were copied to folder called **swissserver** as shown in Figure 14.5:

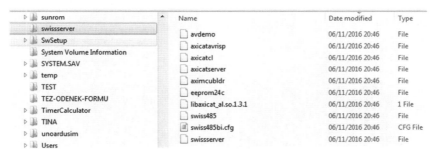

Figure 14.5 Copy the files to folder swissserver on your PC

- Create a new folder on your raspberry Pi called **swissserver** and copy all the files from the PC to this new directory on your Raspberry Pi. It is easier to copy if you use the free **winSCP** file copy program.

- Make the **swissserver** program executable:

    pi@raspberrypi:~ $ **cd swissserver**
    pi@raspberrypi:~ /swissserver $ **chmod + swissserver**

- Start the **swissserver** program on your Raspberry Pi by entering the following command. This command enables us to access the I2C and the RS-485 controller on the Swiss Pi using port number 5003 from Putty. Notice that the ampersand sign at the end of the command ensures that the server program runs in the background so that the keyboard is free to enter other commands:

    pi@raspberrypi:~ /swissserver **$ sudo ./swissserver –i2cdev /dev/ i2c-1 –spidev /dev/spidev0.0 –p 5003 –rs485 spi –crlf&**

You can check whether or not the **swissserver** program is running by entering the following command. The **swisssserver** program should be displayed on the screen if the program is running in the background:

pi@raspberrypi:~ /swissserver **$ ps −a**

14.3.1 Using the I/O Card Explorer Program

An I/O explorer program is available that can be used to set or reset the various modules on the Swiss Pi card interactively. In this section we will load and start the I/O card explorer program on our PC and then set and reset the state of GPIO port A0 interactively. First of all, let us connect an LED to GPIO port A0 of the Swiss Pi card through a 390 ohm current limiting resistor as shown in Figure 14.6.

Figure 14.6 Connect an LED to GPIO port A0

The steps to run the I/O explorer program are given below:

- Go to the following I/O Axiris web site:

    https://www.axiris.eu/en/index.php/free-software/i-o-card-explorer

- Click on the following link to download the I/O explorer program:

    iocardexplorer-1.0.0-win32.zip

Create a new directory on your PC (e.g. **iocardexplorer**) and unzip all the files to this directory as shown in Figure 14.7.

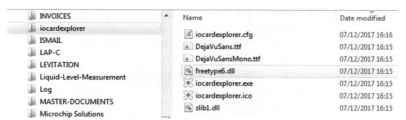

Figure 14.7 Unzip the I/O explorer files

Make sure that the Swiss Pi board is plugged in and also the **swissserver** has been started as described in the previous section. Then start the I/O explorer program by double clicking on file **iocardexplorer.exe** in directory **iocardexplorer**. You should see the screen as in Figure 14.8 (you might have to click the gear shaped icon at the top left hand side of the screen).

Figure 14.8 I/O Card Explorer screen

Enter your Raspberry Pi IP address and the port number as 5003 as was set earlier when the **swissserver** was started. Click the **Connect** button and you should see the **Connected** message as in Figure 14.9.

Figure 14.9 Connected to the Swiss Pi

Click the chip shaped icon at the top left corner of the screen. You should see a screen similar to the one shown in Figure 14.10.

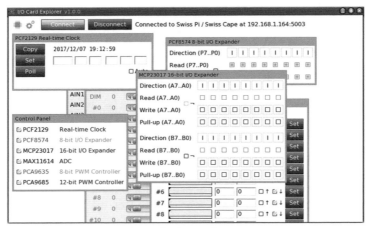

Figure 14.10 I/O explorer screen

Click to set the direction of GPIO port A0 to output (O). Then, click on A0 **Write** to turn the LED ON, and then click again to turn it OFF (see Figure 14.11). This should confirm that the Swiss Pi hardware and software are working correctly.

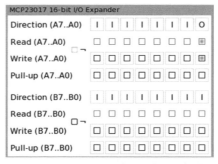

Figure 14.11 Turn the LED ON/OFF

You may like to experiment using other functions of the I/O explorer program.

14.3.2 Using the Swiss Pi From Python

Before using the Swiss Pi from Python we have to import the client module called **textline-netclient** to our default folder on the Raspberry Pi. The steps are given below:

- Go to the Axiris Software Repository web page using your PC:

    https://www.axiris.eu/en/index.php/free-software/software-repository

- Click on the following link to download the Swiss Server program:

    public-2016-11-06-linux-armhf.tar.gz

- Click on the following link:

    public-2016-11-06-src.zip

- Open folders **public**, **swiss**, and **swiss-python**

- Copy file **textlinenetclient.py** to your default home directory (**/home/pi**) on Raspberry Pi so that it can be imported into your Python programs.

Python programs access the Swiss Pi card as client program commands through the Swiss Pi server. Therefore, the server must be started on your Raspberry Pi before you can write and access the Swiss Pi card from Python programs. As shown earlier, the Swiss Pi server is started using the following command (assuming port 5003 is to be used):

pi@raspberrypi:~ /swissserver **$ sudo ./swissserver –i2cdev /dev/i2c-1 – spidev /dev/spidev0.0 –p 5003 –rs485 spi –crlf&**

Full list of the Swiss Pi client commands can be found in the PDF document called **Swiss Server Client Command Protocol** and it can be found at the following link:

https://www.axiris.eu/download/swiss_pi/Swiss_Server_Client_Command_Protocol_spec_en_us_2016_10_26.pdf

A list of some of the useful commands to access the GPIO, ADC, PWM and the Servo of the Swiss Pi card are given below:

GPIO Commands (MCP23017)
iod: Set the direction of one or all I/O pins. The direction of a pin must be set before data can be sent or read from the pin. 0 sets a pin to output, and 1 sets it to input.
iow: Write the output state of one or all I/O pins
ior: Read the state of one or all I/O pins
iopu: Control the pull-up resistor of one or all I/O pins

ADC (MAX11614)
adcr: Read the analog data of all the 8 channels and report the results. The results are also cached.
adcrc: Read one or more cached result.

PWM (PCA9685)
pcr: Read one or more PWM channels
pcw: Write one or more PWM channels
ppw: write the prescaler value
ppr: Read the prescaler value

Servo

>**svme**: Enable servo mode
>**svcw**: Write servo channel
>**svcr**: Read servo channel
>**svmv**: Initiate a servo movement

Additionally, the following commands could be useful:

>**ver**: returns the version number of the client software
>**wait**: waits for a specified period (in milliseconds) before accepting a command
>**close**: Closes the client connection
>**quit**: Quit the server

Before the Swiss Pi card can be accessed, the **textlinenetclient** library must be imported into the program and the server host and the port number must be defined as shown below:

```
import textlinenetclient
host = 'localhost'
port = 5003
```

We must then connect to the swiss server:

```
client = textlinenetclient.TextLineClient(host, port)
```

We can then optionally set the formatting style for all the numbers as:

```
client.sendCmd('norsp vfmts "*" dec 0 0 0 0 0 0 ')
```

The above command sets the formatting style for all the command ("*), the radix in numbers is chosen as decimal (dec), maximum number of digits in numbers are formatted as needed (0), radix character in numbers is not added (0), leading zeroes in numbers are not used (0), numbers do not start with decimal digit (0), uppercase digits in numbers are not used (0), and uppercase radix character is not used in numbers (0).

The command **norsp** can be inserted before the actual command to suppress the return of a response from the server.

Commands are sent to the server using the statement:

```
client.sendCmd
```

where the format of this command is similar to a **print** command. For example, we can set GPIO **pin** to state **on** by the statement:

```
client.sendCmd('norsp iow %d %d'  %(pin, on))
```

14.4 PROJECT 1 – Swiss Pi Based Thermostat with Buzzer

Description: This is a simple thermostat project. In this project an analog temperature sensor chip is connected to one of the ADC ports of the Swiss Pi card. In addition, a buzzer is connected to one of its digital ports. The program activates the buzzer if the temperature gets above 30°C. The temperature is read every 2 seconds.

Aim: The aim of this project is to show how the digital and analog ports of the Swiss Pi card can be used in a project.

Raspberry Pi Type: This project will run on all types of Raspberry Pi with 40 pin GPIO connectors.

Block Diagram: The block diagram of the project is shown in Figure 14.12.

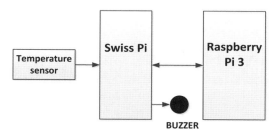

Figure 14.12 Block diagram of the project

Circuit Diagram: Figure 14.13 shows the circuit diagram of the project. A TMP36 type analog temperature sensor chip is connected to analog port 0 of the Swiss Pi card. In addition, an active buzzer is connected to digital port A0. A breadboard is used to make the connections as shown in Figure 14.14.

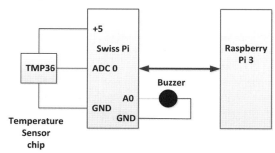

Figure 14.13 Circuit diagram of the project

Figure 14.14 Using a breadboard to connect the sensor and the buzzer

Program: Make sure that the Swiss Pi card is mounted on top of the Raspberry Pi 3. Figure 14.15 shows the program listing (program: swiss1.py). At the beginning of the program, modules time and textlinenetclient are imported to the program and the host and the port names are defined. The program then connects to the Swiss Pi server and sets up the formatting. Variable **pin** is assigned to GPIO port A0 and is set to 0. Variable **dir** is set to 0 which will be used to set the direction of the GPIO port pin. Variables **outputON** and **outputOFF** are defined as 1 and 0 respectively. The GPIO port is then configured as an output and variable **ch** is set to 0 as this will be the ADC channel to be used. The remainder of the program runs in an endless loop. Inside this loop command **adcr** is sent to the Swiss Pi server to read the data of all the 8 ADC channels. The data returned by channel **ch** (0) is then stored in variable **mV**. Notice that the reference voltage of the ADC is +4.096V and its resolution is 12-bits (i.e. 4096 quantization levels). Therefore, the data read from the ADC is directly in millivolts. i.e. **mV** is the actual voltage read from the sensor in millivolts. The temperature is then calculated by subtracting 500 mV and dividing by 10, and rounded to one digit and stored in variable **temp**. The program then checks the temperature and if it is over 30 degrees Centigrade then a command is sent to the Swiss Pi server to activate the buzzer, otherwise the buzzer is turned OFF. The above program loop is repeated after 2 seconds of delay. The temperature is also displayed on the monitor.

```
#-------------------------------------------------------
#
#                 SWISS PI THERMOSTAT
#                 ===================
#
# In this project a TMP36 type analog temperature sensor
```

```
# is connected to analog port A0 of the Swiss Pi card.
# In addition, an active buzzer is connected to digital
# GPIO port A0. The buzzer is activated if the temperature
# gets above 30 degrees Centigrade.The temperature is read
# at every 2 seconds. The temperatue is also displayed on the
# monitor.
#
# Author: Dogan Ibrahim
# Date   : December, 2017
# File   : swiss1.py
#------------------------------------------------------------
import textlinenetclient
import time
#
# Define Swiss Pi server host and port
#
host = 'localhost'
port = 5003


#
# Connect to Swiss Pi server
#
client = textlinenetclient.TextLineNetClient(host,port)


#
# Set up the client
#
client.sendCmd('norsp vfmts "*" dec 0 0 0 0 0 0')


#
# Configure Swiss Pi GPIO A0 (pin 0) as output
#
pin = 0                                    # GPIO pin 0
dir = 0                                    # GPIO pin 0 direction
outputON = 1                               # Output ON state
outputOFF = 0                              # Output OFF state
client.sendCmd('norsp iod %d %d' %(pin,dir)) # Configure direction


#
# Use Swiss Pi ADC channel 0
#
ch = 0


#
# Program loop. Here, the ADC reads the analog data from all the
# 8 channels. The data for channel 0 is converted into millivolts
```

```
# and is then converted into real temperature in degrees centigrade
# If the temperature is greater than 30 degrees Centigrade then the
# buzzer is activated, otherwise the buzzer is set to be OFF. This
# loop is repeated every 2 seconds
#
while True:
    client.sendCmd('adcr', True)                          # start ADC
    tokens = client.tokenizeLine(client.rcvRsp())
    mV = int(tokens[1+ch])                                # get Ch 0 data
    temp = (mV - 500.0) / 10.0                            # convert to C
    temp = round(temp, 1)                                 # round it

    if temp > 30.0:                                       # if > 40 C
        client.sendCmd('norsp iow %d %d' %(pin,outputON)) # set Buzzer ON
    else:
        client.sendCmd('norsp iow %d %d' %(pin,outputOFF))# set buzzer OFF
    print(temp)                                           # display temp
    time.sleep(2)                                         # wait 2 seconds
```

Figure 14.15 Program listing

14.5 PROJECT 2 – Swiss Pi Based DC Motor Speed Control

Description: This is a simple DC motor speed control project. In this project a small DC motor, operating at 5V is connected to PWM channel 0 of the Swiss Pi card. The program increases the duty cycle of the PWM waveform every second and as a result the speed of the motor is increased every second. The duty cycle is changed from 0% to 100%. The motor runs for 5 seconds at 100% duty cycle and the process is then repeated after 10 seconds of delay.

Aim: The aim of this project is to show how the PWM module of the Swiss Pi card can be used in a project.

Raspberry Pi Type: This project will run on all types of Raspberry Pi with 40 pin GPIO connectors.

Block Diagram: The block diagram of the project is shown in Figure 14.16.

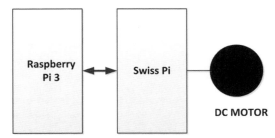

Figure 14.16 Block diagram of the project

Circuit Diagram: Figure 14.17 shows the circuit diagram of the project. The two terminals of the DC motor are connected to channel 0 of the PWM and to GND respectively. Figure 14.18 shows the motor connections to the Swiss Pi card.

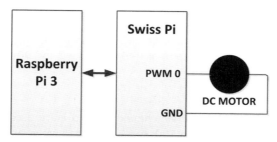

Figure 14.17 Circuit diagram of the project

Figure 14.18 Connecting the motor to the Swiss Pi card

Program: Make sure that the Swiss Pi card is mounted on top of the Raspberry Pi 3 and that the Swiss Pi server is started. Figure 14.19 shows the program listing (program: swiss2.py). At the beginning of the program modules time and textlinenetclient are imported to the program and the host and the port names are defined. The program then connects to the Swiss Pi server and sets up the formatting. Variable **ch** is set to 0 and will be used as the PWM channel. The remainder of the program runs in an endless loop. Inside this loop the duty cycle of the PWM waveform is increased using variable **ON_Number**. The starting ON position of the waveform is set to 0 while the ending position is set by variable **ON_Number**. The initial value of **ON_Number** is set to 1000 so that the starting duty cycle is 1000/4096 i.e. 24% and this value seems just to start the motor. This number is then incremented by 250 until it reaches 4095 which corresponds to 100% duty cycle. At this position the motor is rotated for 5 seconds at full speed. The motor is then stopped for 10 seconds and the above process is repeated.

Notice that the PWM duty cycle is set by the Swiss Pi client command **pcw**. This command has the following format:

pcw first_channel number_of_channels ON flag ON_position OFF_flag OFF_position

The ON and OFF positions can take any value between 0 and 4095. As an example the following command sets the OFF position of PWM channel 2 to 100 and the ON position to 200:

pcw 2 1 0 100 0 200

similarly, in the following command PWM channels 1 and 2 are used. The starting ON and OFF positions of channel 1 are set to 100 and 200 respectively, and the starting ON and OFF positions of channel 2 are set to 150 and 250 respectively:

pcw 1 2 0 100 0 200 0 150 0 250

In the program in Figure 14.19, the following statement is used inside the loop to increment the duty cycle of channel **ch** (0) from 0% to 100%. Here, the starting **ON_Number** is 1000 and is incremented by 250 every second until it is greater than or equal to 4095 (100% duty cycle):

```
ON_Number = 1000
While ON_Number <= 4095:
        client.sendCmd ('norsp  pcw %d 1 0 0 0 %d ' %(ch, ON_Number), True)
        time.sleep(1)
        ON_Number = ON_Number + 250
```

```
#------------------------------------------------------------------
#
#               SWISS PI DC MOTOR SPEED CONTROL
#               ================================
#
# In this project a small 5V operating DC motor is conencted
# to PWM channel 0 of the Swiss Pi card. The program increases
# the PWM duty cycle every second starting from 0% to 100% in
# steps. As a result, the speed of the motor is increased
# gradually. When the motor reaches full speed (100% duty cycle)
# it rotates for 5 seconds and then the process is repeated after
# a delay of 10 seconds.
#
# Author: Dogan Ibrahim
# Date   : December, 2017
# File   : swiss2.py
#------------------------------------------------------------------
import textlinenetclient
import time
```

```
#
# Define Swiss Pi server host and port
#
host = 'localhost'
port = 5003


#
# Connect to Swiss Pi server
#
client = textlinenetclient.TextLineNetClient(host,port)


#
# Set up the client
#
client.sendCmd('norsp vfmts "*" dec 0 0 0 0 0 0')


#
# Use Swiss Pi PWM channel 0 and set ON period to 0 to start with
#
ch = 0


#
# Program loop. Here, the duty cycle of the PWM waveform is
# increased every second so that the motor speed increases.
# When the duty cycle is 100% (i.e. full speed), the motor
# runs for 5 seconds. the process is then repeated after a
# delay of 10 seconds
#
while True:
  ON_Number = 1000
  while ON_Number <= 4095:
    client.sendCmd('norsp pcw %d 1 0 0 0 %d' %(ch, ON_Number), True)
    time.sleep(1)          # 1 second delay
    ON_Number = ON_Number + 250
  time.sleep(5)          # wait 5 seconds
  client.sendCmd('norsp pcw %d 1 0 0 0 %d' %(ch, 0), True)
  time.sleep(10)         # wait 10 seconds
```

Figure 14.19 Program listing

14.6 Summary

In this Chapter we have seen how to use the Swiss Pi card in Raspberry Pi projects. Next Chapter is about using the WiFi of the Raspberry Pi to store the ambient temperature and the humidity on the cloud.

CHAPTER 15 • USING THE WI-FI ON THE RASPBERRY PI 3

15.1 Overview
In this Chapter we shall see how to use measure the ambient temperature and humidity and then send it to the Cloud so that it can be accessed from anywhere.

15.2 PROJECT – Sending the Temperature and Humidity to the Cloud
Description: In this project the Sense HAT board is used to measure the ambient temperature and the humidity (see Chapter 11). The data is then sent to the Cloud by the Raspberry Pi 3.

Aim: The aim of this project is to show how the ambient temperature and humidity readings can be sent to the Cloud through the Wi-Fi of the Raspberry Pi 3.

Raspberry Pi Type: This project will run on the Raspberry Pi 3 and on any other Raspberry Pi that has a 40-pin GPIO connector and an external USB Wi-Fi dongle.

Block Diagram: The block diagram of the project is shown in Figure 15.1.

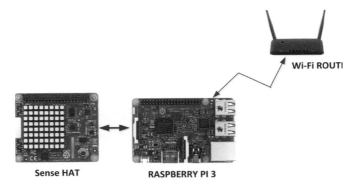

Sense HAT   RASPBERRY PI 3

Figure 15.1 Block diagram of the project

The Cloud
There are several free cloud services that can be used to store data (for example **SparkFun**, **Thingspeak** etc). In this project the **Thingspeak** is used. This is a free Cloud service where sensor data can be stored and retrieved using simple HTTP requests. Before using the Thingspeak, we have to create an account from their web site and then log in to this account. You can create a new account by giving your email address and choose a password by opening the following link:

> https://thingspeak.com/users/sign_up

You should get an email to verify and activate your account. After this, click **Continue** and you should get a successful sign-up notice as shown in Figure 15.2 and you should agree the conditions.

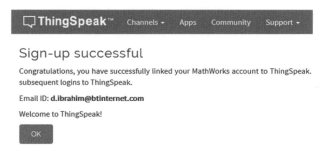

Figure 15.2 Successful sign-up to Thingspeak

Then, you should create a New Channel by clicking on **New Channel**. Fill in the form as shown in Figure 15.3. Give the name **Raspberry Pi 3 Weather** to the application and create two channels called **TEMPERATURE** and **HUMIDITY**. Click **Save Channel** at the bottom of the form

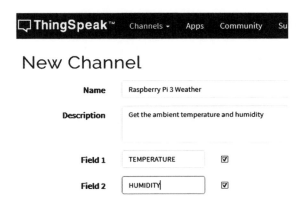

Figure 15.3 Create a New Channel (only part of the form shown)

Now click the **Public View** and then click **Share** and make the channel shearable by every-one so that it is public (see Figure 15.4)

Raspberry Pi 3 Weather

Channel ID: 382058

Author: doganibrahim

Access: Private

Private View   Public View   Channel Settings

Channel Sharing Settings

○ Keep channel view private

◉ Share channel view with everyone

○ Share channel view only with the following users:

Figure 15.4 Make the channel shearable

Click on Public View and you should see your channel details as shown in Figure 15.5.

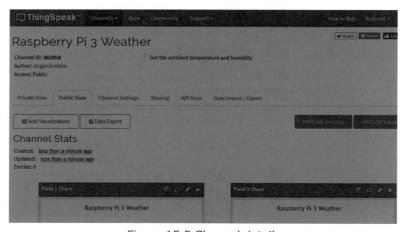

Figure 15.5 Channel details

Your channel is now ready to be used with your data. You should click the **API Keys** tab and save your unique **Write API** and **Read API** keys and the **Channel ID** in a safe place (see Figure 15.6). The **Channel ID** can be displayed by clicking the Channel Details tab. In this example the Channel ID was 382054.

Write API Key

Figure 15.6 API keys

Program: Make sure that the Sense HAT board is mounted on top of the Raspberry Pi 3. Figure 15.7 shows the program listing (program: cloud.py). At the beginning of the program, modules senseHAT, time, and socket are imported into the program and the write API key is defined. Function **TempHun** is created to read and return the ambient temperature and the humidity, rounded to one decimal point. The remainder of the program is executed in an endless loop where a socket is created and the address of the Thingspeak site is obtained. The program then calls function **TempHun** to read the temperature and the humidity. The path to the Thingspeak site is defined and a socket **send** command is issued with the GET parameter to send the temperature and the humidity to the Thingspeak Cloud. The socket is then closed and the process is repeated after 30 seconds of delay.

```
#-----------------------------------------------------------
#              TEMPREATURE AND HUMIDITY ON THE CLOUD
#              =====================================
#
# In this project the Sense HAT board is plugged in on top of
# the Raspberry Pi 3. The program reads the ambient temperature
# and the humidity and sends the data to the cloud every 30
# seconds. The data can be displayed or plotted on the Cloud.
# In this project the free Thingspeak Cloud is used to store and
# display the weather data
#
# Author: Dogan Ibrahim
# File   : cloud.py
# Date   : December, 2017
#-----------------------------------------------------------
import time
import socket
from sense_hat import SenseHat
sense = SenseHat()


#
# Define the Write API key
#
```

```
APIKEY = "H6SXP0DX0XWG0NMV"


#
# Read the ambient temperature and the humidity, round the
# values to 1 digit, and return to teh calling main program
#
def TempHun():
  T = sense.get_temperature()
  H = sense.get_humidity()
  T = round(T, 1)
  H = round(H, 1)
  return T, H


# Start of main program loop. Read the ambient temperature and
# the humidity and then send to the Thingspeak Cloud every 30
# seconds.
#
while True:
  sock = socket.socket()
  addr = socket.getaddrinfo("api.thingspeak.com",80)[0][-1]
  sock.connect(addr)
  (t, h) = TempHun()
  host = "api.thingspeak.com"
  path = "api_key="+APIKEY+"&field1="+str(t)+"&field2="+str(h)
  sock.send(bytes("GET /update?%s HTTP/1.0\r\nHost: %s\r\n\r\n"
   %(path, host)))
  sock.close()
  time.sleep(30)     # wait 30 seconds
```

Figure 15.7 Program listing

Figure 15.8 shows the temperature and the humidity data plotted in real-time. The graphs can be configured by clicking the **Chart Options** on each graph. Figure 15.9 shows the two graphs configured by giving titles to the axes.

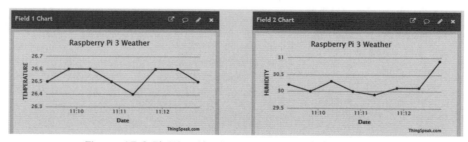

Figure 15.8 Plotting the temperature and the humidity

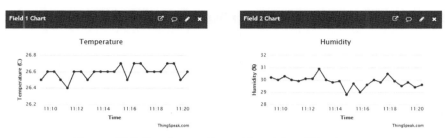

Figure 15.9 Graphs configured by giving titles to axes

The type of plotting can also be changed. Figure 15.10 shows the data shown as column charts.

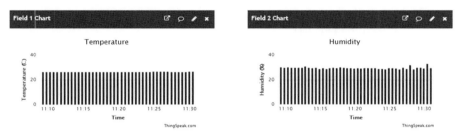

Figure 15.10 Showing the data as column chart

The collected data can be exported to other software packages (e.g. Excel). This is done by clicking the **Data Export** tab.

The following link can be used to access the plotted data externally:

https://api.thingspeak.com/channels/YOUR_CHANNEL_ID

where, for example for this project the channel ID is: 382054. Therefore, the link to the data in this project is:

https://api.thingspeak.com/channels/382054

15.3 Summary
In this Chapter we have seen how to use the Raspbery Pi 3 Wi-Fi to send the ambient temperature and humidity data to the Cloud so that it can be accessed from anywhere. In the next Chapter we will see how to use the Bluetooth module of the Raspberry Pi 3 with an example project.

CHAPTER 16 • USING THE BLUETOOTH ON THE RASPBERRY PI 3

16.1 Overview

In this Chapter we shall see how to use the Bluetooth on the Raspberry Pi 3 in a simple project.

16.2 PROJECT – Bluetooth Control of Buzzer and LED From a Mobile Phone

Description: In this project a buzzer and an LED are connected to the Raspberry Pi 3 and they are controlled by sending commands from an Android mobile phone using Bluetooth for communication.

The following commands can be sent from the Android mobile phone to control the LED and the Buzzer:

L1	Turn the LED ON
L0	Turn the LED OFF
B1	Turn the Buzzer ON
B0	Turn the Buzzer OFF

Aim: The aim of this project is to show how the Bluetooth of the Raspberry Pi 3 can be used in a project.

Raspberry Pi Type: This project will run on the Raspberry Pi 3 and on any other Raspberry Pi that has a 40-pin GPIO connector and an external USB Bluetooth dongle.

Block Diagram: The block diagram of the project is shown in Figure 16.1.

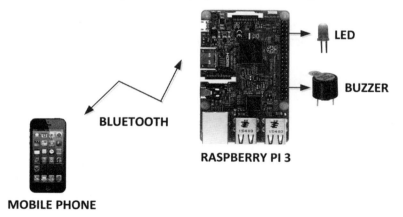

Figure 16.1 Block diagram of the project

Circuit Diagram: The circuit diagram of the project is shown in Figure 16.2 The LED and the Buzzer are connected to GPIO ports 2 and 3 respectively.

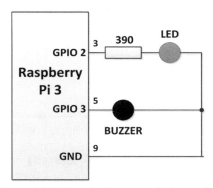

Figure 16.2 Circuit diagram of the project

Bluetooth On Raspberry Pi 3
In this project we shall be sending commands from an Android mobile phone to our Raspberry Pi 3. We must therefore first of all enable Bluetooth from the Settings menu on our Android device. In this example the Android Bluetooth device name is **VFD900**.

There are two ways you can enable Bluetooth on the Raspberry Pi 3: using graphical desktop (GUI mode), or using the command mode.

Using the Graphical Desktop
The steps for enabling Bluetooth on the Raspberry Pi 3 using the graphical desktop are given below:

- Start the VNC server on your Raspberry Pi 3 and login using the VNC Viewer.

- Click on the Bluetooth icon on your Raspberry Pi 3 screen at the top right hand side, and turn Bluetooth ON. Then, select **Make Discoverable.** You should see the Bluetooth icon flashing (Figure 16.3)

Figure 16.3 Enable Bluetooth on your Raspberry Pi 3

- Select **raspberrypi** in the Bluetooth menu (**raspberrypi** is the default Bluetooth name of your Raspberry Pi 3) on your mobile device. You should see the **Connecting** message on your mobile device.

- Accept the pairing request on your Raspberry Pi 3 as shown in Figure 16.4

Figure 16.4 Bluetooth pairing request

You should now see the message **Connected Successfully** on your Raspberry Pi 3

Using Command Mode
You can enable Bluetooth on your Raspberry Pi 3 using the command mode. Additionally you can make Bluetooth discoverable, scan for nearby Bluetooth devices and then connect to a Bluetooth device. The steps are given below (characters types by the user are in bold for clarity):

- Make your Bluetooth discoverable with the following command:

    pi@raspberrypi: ~ $ **sudo hciconfig hci0 piscan**

- Start the Bluetooth tool on your Raspberry Pi 3 from the command mode:

    pi@raspberrypi:~ $ **bluetoothctl**

- Turn Bluetooth ON:

    [bluetooth]# **power on**

- Configure Bluetooth to run:

    [bluetooth]# **agent on**
    [bluetooth]# **default-agent**

- Make device discoverable:

    [bluetooth]# **discoverable on**

- Scan for nearby Bluetooth devices. You should see the nearby Bluetooth devices listed with their MAC addresses. Make a note of the MAC address of the device you wish to connect to (Android mobile phone in this project) as we will be using this address to connect to the device. An example is shown in Figure 16.5:

    [bluetooth]# **scan on**

```
pi@raspberrypi:~ $ bluetoothctl
[NEW] Controller B8:27:EB:25:87:C9 raspberrypi [default]
[bluetooth]# power on
Changing power on succeeded
[bluetooth]# agent on
Agent registered
[bluetooth]# scan on
Discovery started
[   ] Controller B8:27:EB:25:87:C9 Discovering: yes
[NEW] Device A4:77:33:BD:1A:7F A4-77-33-BD-1A-7F
[   ] Device A4:77:33:BD:1A:7F Name: Chromecast7872
[   ] Device A4:77:33:BD:1A:7F Alias: Chromecast7872
[bluetooth]# █
```

Figure 16.5 Scanning nearby devices

In this example our mobile phone is VFD900 and the Bluetooth MAC address is: 28:BE:03:7A:53:F5

- Pair the device:

  [bluetooth]# **pair 28:BE:03:7A:53:F5**

- Connect to our mobile phone:

  [bluetooth]# **connect 28:BE:03:7A:53:F5**

- Exit from the Bluetooth tool by entering Cntrl+Z

  You can find the Bluetooth MAC address of your Raspberry Pi 3 by entering the following command:

  pi@raspberrypi:~ $ **hciconfig | grep "BD Address"**

  You can change the Bluetooth broadcast name by the following command:

  pi@raspberrypi:~ $ **sudo hciconfig hci0 name "new name"**

To see your Bluetooth broadcast name, enter:

  pi@raspberrypi:~ $ **sudo hciconfig hci0 name**

Some other useful Raspberry Pi 3 Bluetooth commands are:

- To reset Bluetooth adapter: **sudo hciconfig hci0 reset**
- To restart Bluetooth: **sudo invoke-rc.d bluetooth restart**
- To list Bluetooth adapters: **hciconfig**

You can find the Bluetooth MAC address of your Android phone as follows:

- Go to **Settings** menu

- Tap **About Phone**
- Tap **Status**
- Scroll down to see your **Bluetooth address**

Python Bluetooth Library

You will need to install the Python Bluetooth library before developing your program. This is done by entering the following command in the command mode:

pi@raspberrypi:~ $ **sudo apt-get install python-bluez**

Accessing From the Mobile Phone

In order to be able to access the Raspberry Pi 3 from a mobile phone apps make the following changes to your Raspberry Pi 3 from the command line:

- Start nano to edit the following file:

  pi@raspberrypi:~ $ **sudo nano /etc/systemd/system/dbus-org. bluez.service**

- Add –C at the end of the ExecStart= line. Also add another line after the ExecStart line. The final two lines should look like:

  ExecStart=/usr/lib/bluetooth/bluetoothd -C
  ExecStartPost=/usr/bin/sdptool add SP

- Exit and save the file by entering Ctrl+X and Y

- Reboot Raspberry Pi 3:

  pi@raspberrypi:~ $ **sudo reboot**

Android Bluetooth Apps

In this project we will be sending commands to the Raspberry Pi 3 from an Android based mobile phone. We therefore need an application on our mobile phone where we can send data through Bluetooth. There are many such applications free of charge in the Android **Play Store**. The one chosen by the author is called **Arduino Bluetooth Controller** by **Khondokar Production** (see Figure 16.6). You should install this application (or a similar one) on your Android phone so that you can send commands to the Raspberry Pi 3.

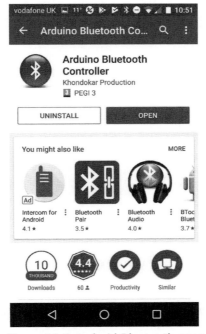

Figure 16.6 Android Bluetooth apps

Program: Figure 16.7 shows the program listing of the project (program: bluetooth.py). At the beginning of the program modules socket, RPi.GPIO, and Bluetooth are imported to the program. The LED and Buzzer ports are defined and both configured as outputs. The program then creates a Bluetooth socket, binds and listens on this socket, and then waits to accept a connection. The remainder of the program is executed in a loop where the program issues statement **ClientSock.recv** and waits to read data from the mobile phone. The received data is decoded and the LED and the Buzzer are turned ON or OFF as requested.

```
#-------------------------------------------------------------
#               BLUETOOTH BASED CONTROL
#               ========================
#
# In this project an LED and a Buzzer are connected to GPIO ports
# GPIO 2 and GPIO 3 of the Raspberry Pi 3 respectively. The LED
# and the Buzzer are controlled by sedning comamnds from an Android
# mobile phone using the Bluetooth communication. The commands are
# sent using a Bluetooth apps on the Android mobile phone.
#
# The following are the valid commands:
#
# L1 Turn the LED ON
# L0 Turn the LED OFF
# B1 Turn the Buzzer ON
```

```
# B0 Turn the Buzzer OFF
#
# Author: Dogan Ibrahim
# File   : bluetooth.py
# Date   : December, 2017
#-------------------------------------------------------------
import socket
import RPi.GPIO as GPIO
GPIO.setwarnings(False)
GPIO.setmode(GPIO.BCM)
import bluetooth

#
# LED is on GPIO2, Buzzer is on GPIO3
#
LED = 2            # LED on GPIO2
Buzzer = 3          # Buzzer on GPIO3

#
# Configure LED and Buzzer as outputs
#
GPIO.setup(LED, GPIO.OUT)
GPIO.setup(Buzzer, GPIO.OUT)

#
# Turn OFF LED and Buzzer to start with
#
GPIO.output(LED, 0)
GPIO.output(Buzzer, 0)

#
# Start of main program loop. Read commands from the Android
# mobile phone, decode them, and control the LED and the Buzzer
# as requested by the command
#
Port = 1
ServerSock = bluetooth.BluetoothSocket(bluetooth.RFCOMM)
ServerSock.bind(("", Port))
ServerSock.listen(1)
ClientSock, addr = ServerSock.accept()

#
# Turn ON the LED if the command is     L1
# Turn OFF the LED if the command is    L0
# Turn ON the Buzzer if the command is  B1
# Turn OFF the Buzzer if the command is B0
```

```
#
while True:
  data = ClientSock.recv(1024)
  if data[0] == 'L':
    if data[1] == '1':
      GPIO.output(LED, 1)
    else:
      GPIO.output(LED, 0)
  elif data[0] == 'B':
    if data[1] == '1':
      GPIO.output(Buzzer, 1)
    else:
      GPIO.output(Buzzer, 0)
```

Figure 16.7 Program listing

Figure 16.8 shows the mobile application sending a command to turn the LED ON by sending command L1. Notice that you must start the Raspberry Pi 3 program before starting the mobile application.

Figure 16.8 Mobile application

You could enter the program name in the following format inside file **/etc/rc.local** so that the program starts automatically after the Raspberry Pi 3 re-starts:

python /home/pi/bluet.py &

When you finish your project don't forget to remove the above line from file **/etc/rc.local**, otherwise the program will run every time your Raspberry Pi 3 is re-started. You should also shutdown your Raspberry Pi 3 orderly instead of just removing the power cable. The command to shutdown orderly is:

```
pi@raspberrypi:~ $ sudo shutdown -h now
```

16.3 Summary

In this Chapter the use of the Raspberry Pi 3 Bluetooth module has been described with a simple project.

APPENDIX A • RASPBERRY PI 3 GPIO PIN CONFIGURATION

Raspberry Pi 3 GPIO Header

Pin#	NAME		NAME	Pin#
01	3.3v DC Power		DC Power 5v	02
03	GPIO02 (SDA1 , I²C)		DC Power 5v	04
05	GPIO03 (SCL1 , I²C)		Ground	06
07	GPIO04 (GPIO_GCLK)		(TXD0) GPIO14	08
09	Ground		(RXD0) GPIO15	10
11	GPIO17 (GPIO_GEN0)		(GPIO_GEN1) GPIO18	12
13	GPIO27 (GPIO_GEN2)		Ground	14
15	GPIO22 (GPIO_GEN3)		(GPIO_GEN4) GPIO23	16
17	3.3v DC Power		(GPIO_GEN5) GPIO24	18
19	GPIO10 (SPI_MOSI)		Ground	20
21	GPIO09 (SPI_MISO)		(GPIO_GEN6) GPIO25	22
23	GPIO11 (SPI_CLK)		(SPI_CE0_N) GPIO08	24
25	Ground		(SPI_CE1_N) GPIO07	26
27	ID_SD (I²C ID EEPROM)		(I²C ID EEPROM) ID_SC	28
29	GPIO05		Ground	30
31	GPIO06		GPIO12	32
33	GPIO13		Ground	34
35	GPIO19		GPIO16	36
37	GPIO26		GPIO20	38
39	Ground		GPIO21	40

Rev. 2
29/02/2016   www.element14.com/RaspberryPi

Figure A1 - www.element14.com

APPENDIX B • ANDROID APPS FOR THE RASPBERRY PI

There a number of Raspberry Pi apps available for the Android mobile phones that can be useful while working with the Raspberry Pi. In this Appendix we shall be looking at some of these apps. All of these apps were available on the **Play Store** at the time of writing this book.

B.1 Fing
This apps can be used to scan and find the IP address of all the devices connected to your Wi-Fi router. It is especially useful to find the IP address of your Raspberry Pi. A sample display is shown in Figure B1 where the Wi=Fi router name was BTHub5-6SPN-5G and IP address of the Raspberry Pi is shown as 192.168.1.164

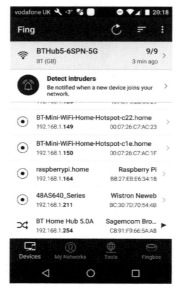

Figure B.1 Fing display

B.2 Raspi Check
Using this apps you can login to your Raspberry Pi and then get real-time information about the system. Some of the features displayed are (see Figure B.2):

- Core temperature. frequency, and voltage
- System memory, serial number etc.
- Network details
- Disk usage
- Processes

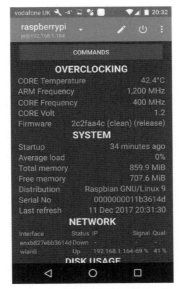

Figure B.2 Raspi Check display

B.3 VNC Viewer

This apps enables you to connect to the Raspberry Pi via the VNC Viewer so that you can have access to the desktop GUI. You will have to register so that you can use this apps. Before using this apps make sure that the VNCserver is started on your Raspberr Pi with the command:

```
pi@raspberrypi:~ $ vncserver :1
```

When entering the IP address of your Raspberry Pi on the VNC Viewer apps, terminate the address with a colon followed by 1. For example:

```
192.168.1.164:1
```

Figure B.3 shows the VNC Viewer apps after logging in.

Figure B.3 VNC Viewer display

B.4 RPiREF

RPiREF is a simple apps that identifies all the pins on the Raspberry Pi. The pin numbers, GPIO numbers, and alternate functions are displayed. Figure B.4 shows the RPiREF display.

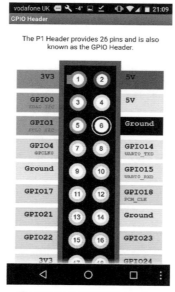

Figure B.4 RPiREF display

B.5 Mobile SSH

This apps is useful for making SSH type connections to your Raspberry Pi. Figure B.5 shows a typical display.

Figure B.5 Mobile SSH display

B.6 Pi HealthCheck

This is another useful apps that displays information about the state of your Raspberry Pi computer. A typical display is shown in Figure B.6.

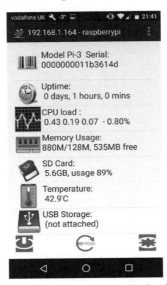

Figure B.6 Pi HealthCheck display

Index